# Fundamental Engineering Thermodynamics

David Dunn

CU01082356

# Fundamental Engineering Thermodynamics

**David Dunn**

Longman

**Pearson Education Limited**
Edinburgh Gate, Harlow
Essex CM20 2JE, England
*and Associated Companies throughout the world*

First published 2001

**British Library Cataloguing in Publication Data**
A catalogue entry for this title is available from the British Library

ISBN 0-582-43217-0

Set by 35 in Times 10/12 and Frutiger

Transferred to digital print on demand, 2006

Printed and bound by Antony Rowe Ltd, Eastbourne

# Contents

# Preface

Modern society uses vast quantities of energy. We use energy to heat our homes. We use energy to power our cars, trains and aeroplanes. We use energy to provide electricity to our homes and factories. The primary source of this energy is mainly fossil or nuclear fuel. Hydro-electric power is also an important source of energy but unfortunately most mountains and lakes are not located in the populated areas where the energy is needed most. In order to convert this primary source of energy into the form we need, we must at some point convert it into mechanical power in the form of a rotating shaft. An example of this is the shaft connecting a gas or steam turbine to the electric generator in the power station. Other examples are the shafts connecting car engines to their wheels and ships' engines to their propellers.

The energy stored in fossil and nuclear fuels cannot be converted into mechanical energy without first turning it into heat at a hot temperature using combustion or fission. The only natural (renewable) sources of hot heat are solar (from the sun) and geothermal (from deep within the earth). The real problem for the engineer is how to convert this hot heat into mechanical power and this requires a heat engine and a good understanding of the science of thermodynamics.

It has been said that the science of thermodynamics owes more to the steam engine than the steam engine owes to the science. Today's modern heat engines owe much to such pioneers as Richard Trevithick and James Watt who developed steam engines. Otto and Diesel pioneered internal combustion engines and others before them investigated ways and means of turning heat into work. As long ago as 120 BC, Hero of Alexandria constructed a simple steam turbine. It took the industrial revolution and the need for greater power than could be obtained from windmills and water wheels to really get things going.

Thermodynamics and the closely linked subject of fluid mechanics have come to be regarded as difficult subjects and are shunned on many engineering courses at all levels. This is a sad development because it is such an important subject with widespread applications. Thermodynamics at its purest level is a very mathematical subject and unless you have a very good comprehension of maths, the classic texts are somewhat overwhelming. In my experience, students often get stuck in their studies because they have missed some basic point regarded as too simple to be covered in the classical textbooks.

There are many jobs for engineers with a good comprehension of thermodynamics. They are needed to operate and design our power stations, our next generation of engines for ships, vehicles, aeroplanes and rockets. They are needed to lead the way in developing renewable energy sources and making what we do more energy efficient.

I have attempted to make this book simple and interesting and hope that it will get you through the Edexcel Higher National module, the first year of your degree or the part 1 Engineering Council exam. I have taken some short cuts and liberties that may not be to the liking of the experts, but if I succeed in getting you interested in the subject you should be able to understand the classic textbooks better and go a lot further.

**David Dunn**

# Aims

This book meets all the requirements of the Edexcel module 'Engineering Thermodynamics' (Unit code: 21769P). It also includes prerequisite studies and additional material that makes it suitable for degree level studies. The material is also suitable for the Engineering Council Part 1 exam in Thermodynamics and provides a foundation for the Part 2 exam.

The four outcomes covered are as follows.

## *Outcome 1: Thermodynamic systems*

- **Polytropic processes**: general equation $pV^n = C$, relationships between index $n$ and heat transfer during a process, constant pressure and reversible isothermal and adiabatic processes, expressions for work flow
- **Properties**: intensive, extensive, two-property rule
- **Thermodynamic systems**: closed systems, open systems, application of the first law to derive system energy equations
- **Relationship**: $R = c_p - c_v$ and $\gamma = c_p/c_v$

## *Outcome 2: Internal combustion engines*

- **Second law of thermodynamics**: statement of law, schematic representation of a heat engine to show heat and work flow
- **Heat engine cycles**: Carnot cycle, Otto cycle, Diesel cycle, dual combustion cycle, Joule cycle, property diagrams, Carnot efficiency, air-standard efficiency
- **Performance characteristics**: engine trials, mean effective pressure, indicated and brake power, indicated and brake thermal efficiency, mechanical efficiency, specific fuel consumption, heat balance
- **Improvements**: supercharging, turbocharging and intercooling, cooling system and exhaust gas heat recovery systems

## *Outcome 3: Air compressors*

- **Property diagrams**: theoretical pressure–volume diagrams for single and multi-stage compressors; actual indicator diagrams, actual isothermal and adiabatic compression curves, induction and delivery effects of clearance volume

---

- **Performance characteristics**: free air delivery, volumetric efficiency, actual and isothermal work done per cycle, isothermal efficiency
- **First law of thermodynamics**: input power, air power, heat transfer to intercooler and aftercooler, energy balance
- **Faults and hazards**: effects of water in compressed air, causes of compressor fires and explosions

## Outcome 4: Steam and gas turbine

- **Principles of operation**: impulse and reaction turbines, condensing, pass-out and back-pressure steam turbines, single- and double-shaft gas turbines, regeneration and reheat in gas turbines, combined heat and power plants
- **Circuit and property diagrams**: circuit diagrams to show boiler/heat exchanger, superheater, turbine, condenser, condenser cooling water circuit, hotwell, economiser/feedwater heater, condensate extraction and boiler feed pumps, temperature–entropy diagram of Rankine cycle
- **Performance characteristics**: Carnot and Rankine cycle efficiencies, turbine isentropic effciency, power output, use of property tables and enthalpy–entropy diagram for steam

# Nomenclature

The symbols used throughout in these tutorials are expressed in SI units. This system recommends the use of '/' to mean divide rather than the use of negative indices. For example m/s rather than $ms^{-1}$.

| Quantity | Units | Derived unit | SI symbol |
|---|---|---|---|
| Length | m (metre) | – | various |
| Mass | kg (kilogram) | – | $m$ |
| Time | s (second) | – | $t$ |
| Absolute temperature | K (kelvin) | – | $T$ |
| Celsius temperature | °C | – | $\theta$ |
| Volume | $m^3$ | – | $V$ or $Q$ |
| Specific volume | $m^3/kg$ | – | $v$ |
| Volume flow rate | $m^3/s$ | – | – |
| Density | $kg/m^3$ | – | $\rho$ |
| Mass flow rate | kg/s | – | – |
| Force | $kg\ m/s^2$ | N (newton) | $F$ |
| Weight | $kg\ m/s^2$ | N | $W$ |
| Pressure head | m | – | $h$ |
| Altitude | m | – | $z$ |
| Area | $m^2$ | – | $A$ |
| Velocity | m/s | – | $v$ or $u$ |
| Acceleration | $m/s^2$ | – | $a$ |
| Pressure | $N/m^2$ | Pa (pascal) | $p$ |
| Energy | N m | J (joule) | – |
| Enthalpy | N m | J | $H$ |
| Internal energy | N m | J | $U$ |
| Heat transfer | N m | J | $Q$ |
| Work | N m | J | $W$ |
| Heat transfer rate | N m/s | W (watt) | $\Phi$ |
| Work rate (power) | N m/s | W | $P$ |
| Specific enthalpy | N m/kg | J/kg | $h$ |
| Specific internal energy | N m/kg | J/kg | $u$ |
| Specific heat capacity | N m/kg K | J/kg K | $C$ |
| Characteristic gas constant | N m/kg K | J/kg K | $R$ |
| Entropy | J/K | – | $S$ |

| Specific entropy | J/kg K | – | $s$ |
| Universal gas constant | J/kmol K | – | $R_0$ |
| Dynamic viscosity | N s/m$^2$ | Pa s | $\eta$ or $\mu$ |
| Kinematic viscosity | m$^2$/s | – | $v$ |
| Polytropic index | – | – | $n$ |
| Adiabatic index | – | – | $\gamma$ |

# Acknowledgements

The author and publishers are grateful to the following organisations for permission to reproduce the photographs used in this book.

- British Nuclear Fuels Magnox for our Fig. 5.7 (Sizewell A Power Station).
- GEC-Alsthom for our Fig. 5.8.
- Atlas Copco for Fig. 4.1.

# 1 Properties of fluids

Students of thermodynamics must fully understand the properties of fluids and how to find them. When you have completed this chapter, you should be able to:

- Calculate the energy of a fluid.
- Explain and use the relationship between flow rate and velocity of a fluid.
- Find the properties of liquids, gases and vapours.
- Explain and use the specific heats of gases.

## 1.1 General properties

### 1.1.1 *Extensive and intensive properties*

Throughout these tutorials, you will use properties that are either **extensive** or **intensive**.

An extensive property is one that is divisible. For example, a volume when divided by a number becomes a smaller volume. Other examples are mass and energy.

An intensive property is a property of a mass that remains the same value when the mass is divided into smaller parts. For example, the temperature and density of a substance is unchanged if it is divided into smaller masses.

### 1.1.2 *Total and specific properties*

Throughout these tutorials you will use **total** and **specific** quantities which relate only to extensive properties. A total quantity is always denoted by a higher case letter such as $V$ for volume ($m^3$) and $H$ for enthalpy (J). Specific quantities represent the quantity per kg, and are obtained by dividing the property by the mass. Such properties are always designated by lower case letters such as $v$ for specific volume ($m^3/kg$) and $h$ for specific enthalpy (J/kg).

Specific volume is mainly used for gas and vapours. The inverse of specific volume is density ($\rho$ $kg/m^3$) and although this is mainly used for liquids and solids, it is also used for gases. Note $\rho = 1/v$.

Because the same letters are used to designate more than one property, alternative letters are often used. For example, $v$ for specific volume may occur in the same work as $v$ for velocity, so $u$ or $c$ may also be used for velocity. $h$ is used for height, head and specific enthalpy, so $z$ is often used for height instead.

### 1.1.3 *Two-property rule*

You will study the thermodynamic properties of liquids, gases and vapours in the following sections. Finding the properties of fluids is essential if you are to solve problems that involve them. If we know two independent properties of a substance, then the others may be determined: this is the two-property rule. For example, if we know the temperature and pressure of a gas, we can calculate the volume. The exception to this rule is when a substance undergoes a change in state, such as during evaporation or condensation.

The remainder of this chapter covers the properties of fluids. If you already understand this, you should go to Chapter 2.

## 1.2 Energy forms

A fluid may possess several forms of energy:

- **Internal energy**. This may be considered as the energy a fluid possesses because of its temperature.
- **Gravitational** or **potential energy**. This is the energy of the fluid due to its height above some datum level.
- **Kinetic energy**. This is energy due to the fluid's velocity, and hence only applies to fluids in motion.
- **Flow energy**. This is the energy that is put into a fluid when it is pressurised and transported to another location by flowing.
- **Enthalpy**. Pressure and temperature are usually the main two governing factors and we add internal energy to flow energy in order to produce a single entity called enthalpy.

Let us look at each form in more detail.

### 1.2.1 *Gravitational or potential energy*

In order to raise a mass $m$ kg a height $z$ metres, a lifting force is required which must be at least equal to the weight $mg$ (Fig. 1.1).

**Fig. 1.1** *Gravitational energy*

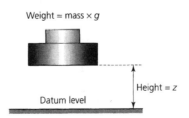

Weight = mass × g

Height = z

Datum level

The work done raising the mass is force × distance moved, so

Work = $mgz$

Since energy has been used to do this work and we know that energy cannot be destroyed, it follows that the energy must be stored in the mass and we call this gravitational energy or potential energy, PE. This energy can be stored and retrieved at will by, for example, a hydro-electric power station.

PE = $mgz$

### 1.2.2 *Kinetic energy*

When a mass $m$ kg is accelerated from rest to a velocity of $v$ m/s (e.g. a bullet in a gun barrel), a force is needed to accelerate it (Fig. 1.2). This is given by Newton's Second Law of Motion, $F = ma$.

**Fig. 1.2** *Kinetic energy*

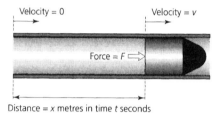

Velocity = 0    Velocity = $v$

Force = $F$

Distance = $x$ metres in time $t$ seconds

After a time of $t$ seconds the mass travels $x$ metres and reaches a velocity of $v$ m/s. The laws relating these quantities are $a = v/t$ and $x = vt/2$.

The work done is

$$W = Fx = max = m\frac{v}{t}v\frac{t}{2} = \frac{mv^2}{2}$$

The energy that has been used to do this work must be stored in the mass and carried along with it. This is **kinetic energy**:

$$\text{KE} = \frac{mv^2}{2}$$

### 1.2.3 *Flow energy*

When a fluid is pumped along a pipe, energy is used to do the pumping. This energy is carried along in the fluid and may be recovered (as, for example, with an air tool or a hydraulic motor). Consider a piston pushing fluid into a cylinder as shown, for example, in Fig. 1.3.

The fluid pressure is $p$ N/m², and the force needed on the piston is $F = pA$. The piston moves a distance $x$ metres. The work done is

$$W = Fx = pAx$$

**Fig. 1.3** *Flow energy*

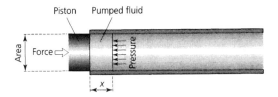

Since $Ax = V$, and is the volume pumped into the cylinder, the work done is

$$W = pV$$

Since energy has been used to do this work, it must now be stored in the fluid and carried along with it as **flow energy**:

$$FE = pV$$

### 1.2.4 *Internal energy*

This is covered in more detail later. The molecules of a fluid possess kinetic energy and potential energy relative to some internal datum. This is usually regarded as the energy due to the temperature and the change in internal energy in a fluid that undergoes a change in temperature is often given by

$$\Delta U = mc\,\Delta T$$

The symbol for internal energy is $U$ kJ or $u$ kJ/kg. Note that a change in temperature is the same in degrees Celsius or Kelvin. The law that states that internal energy is a function of temperature only is known as **Joule's law**.

### 1.2.5 *Enthalpy*

When a fluid has pressure and temperature, it must possess both flow and internal energy. It is often convenient to add them together, and the result is **enthalpy**, which is denoted by $H$ kJ or $h$ kJ/kg.

$$H = FE + U$$

At this stage, you are not yet in a position to do any meaningful calculations. You must first study the properties of fluids and the laws relating them.

## 1.3 Continuity of flow

When a fluid flows in a pipe, the volumetric flow rate is the product of mean velocity and area (Fig. 1.4) such that:

volume per second = area × velocity, i.e.   $V = Av$

The mass flow rate is obtained by multiplying the volume by the density, so

$$m = \rho Av$$

**Fig. 1.4** *Continuity of flow*

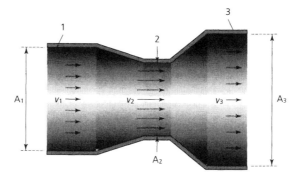

If the area changes the mass remains constant, therefore the velocity must change. In the case of liquids, the density is constant, but not in the case of vapours or gases.

$$\rho_1 A_1 v_1 = \rho_2 A_2 v_2 = \rho_3 A_3 v_3$$

This equation will be needed to enable you to calculate the velocity, and hence kinetic energy, of a fluid.

## WORKED EXAMPLE 1.1

A pipe of 50 mm bore diameter carries water with a mean velocity of 4 m/s and a pressure of 200 kPa. The density of water is 1000 kg/m³. Calculate:

(a)  The volumetric flow rate.
(b)  The mass flow rate.
(c)  The kinetic energy per second.
(d)  The flow energy per second.

If the bore diameter of the pipe reduces to 25 mm, calculate the new velocity.

**Solution**
$A_1 = \pi d^2/4 = (\pi \times 50^2)/4 = 1963.5 \text{ mm}^2$   or   $1.9635 \times 10^{-3} \text{ m}^2$
Volumetric flow rate $= Q = A_1 v_1 = 1.9635 \times 10^{-3} \times 4 = 7.854 \times 10^{-3} \text{ m}^3/\text{s}$

$m = \text{density} \times \text{volume} = \rho Q = 1000 \times 7.854 \times 10^{-3} = 7.854 \text{ kg/s}$

Kinetic energy/s $= mv^2/2 = (7.854 \times 4^2)/2 = 493.5 \text{ W}$
Flow energy/s $= pQ = 200\,000 \times 7.854 \times 10^{-3} = 1571 \text{ W}$

$A_2 = \pi d^2/4 = (\pi \times 25^2)/4 = 490.87 \text{ mm}^2$

$\rho_1 A_1 v_1 = \rho_2 A_2 v_2$    But   $\rho_1 = \rho_2$

$\therefore \quad v_2 = A_1 v_1 / A_2 = (1963.5 \times 4)/490.87 = 16 \text{ m/s}$

1.  3 kg/s of a fluid flows in a pipe with a mean velocity of 5 m/s. Calculate the kinetic energy conveyed per second.

2.  4 m³/s of a fluid flows in a duct with a pressure of 2 MPa. Calculate the flow energy conveyed per second.

3.  400 kg of fluid is pumped from one lake to another 400 m higher in altitude. What is the increase in energy?

4.  0.128 m³/s of gas flows at 12 m/s velocity and 2 MPa pressure at 25 °C. Calculate:
    (a) the kinetic energy being transported per second
    (b) the flow energy being transported per second.

5.  A duct has a cross-sectional area of 0.08 m² and carries gas at a velocity of 9 m/s. If the duct reduces to a cross-sectional area of 0.3 m², calculate the velocity in the smaller section, assuming the density is constant.

6.  A liquid flows in a pipe at a rate of 1.7 kg/s and a pressure of 0.5 MPa. The pipe has a bore of 20 mm diameter. The liquid has a density of 800 kg/m³. Calculate the following:
    (a) The velocity of the liquid.
    (b) The kinetic energy per second.
    (c) The flow energy per second.

## 1.4 Gas laws

In this section you will

- Derive basic gas laws.
- Examine the characteristic gas law.
- Examine the universal gas law.
- Define the kilomole.
- Solve gas law problems.

### 1.4.1 *Theory for perfect gases*

A gas is made of molecules that move around with random motion. In a perfect gas, the molecules may collide but they have no tendency to stick together or repel each other. In other words, a perfect gas is completely inviscid. In reality, there is a slight force of attraction between gas molecules but this is so small that gas laws formulated for an ideal gas work quite well for a real gas.

Each molecule in the gas has an instantaneous velocity and hence has kinetic energy. The sum of this energy is the internal energy $U$. The velocity of the molecules depends upon the temperature. When the temperature changes, so does the internal energy. The internal energy is, for all intents and purposes, zero at −273 °C, which is

**Fig. 1.5** *Kinetic theory of gases*

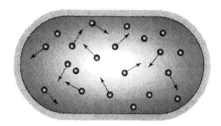

the absolute zero of temperature. Remember that to convert from Celcius to absolute (Kelvin), add 273. For example

40 °C = 40 + 273 = 313 K.

### 1.4.2 *Pressure*

If a gas is compressed it obtains pressure. This is best explained by considering a gas inside a vessel, as shown in Fig. 1.5.

The gas molecules bombard the inside of the container, and each produces a momentum force when it bounces. The force per unit area is the pressure of the gas. Remember that

Pressure = force/area
$p = F/A$ N/m² (or Pascal)

Note that: $10^3$ Pa = 1 kPa;   $10^6$ Pa = 1 MPa;   $10^5$ Pa = 1 bar

### 1.4.3 *Constant volume law*

If a gas is heated, the velocity of the gas molecules increases. If the container is rigid, the molecules will hit the surface more often and with greater force, so we expect the increase in pressure to be proportional to the increase in temperature:

**$p = cT$   when $V$ is constant**

---

**WORKED EXAMPLE 1.2**

A mass of gas has a pressure of 500 kPa and a temperature of 150 °C. If the pressure is changed to 900 kPa with no change in volume, determine the new temperature.

*Solution*
Using the constant volume law, find

$p_1/T_1 = c = p_2/T_2$

where   $T_1 = 150 + 273 = 423$ K
$p_1 = 500\ 000$
$p_2 = 900\ 000$
$T_2 = p_2 T_1/p_1 = 900\ 000 \times 423/500\ 000 = 761.4$ K

---

## 1.4.4 Charles's law

If we kept the pressure constant and increased the temperature, then we would have to make the volume bigger in order to stop the pressure rising. This gives us Charles's law:

$V = cT$   **when $p$ is constant**

---

**WORKED EXAMPLE 1.3**

A mass of gas has a temperature of 150 °C and volume of 0.2 m³. If the temperature is changed to 50 °C with no change in pressure, determine the new volume.

*Solution*
Using Charles's law, we find

$$V_1/T_1 = c = V_2/T_2$$

where   $T_1 = 150 + 273 = 423$ K
$V_1 = 0.2$
$T_2 = 50 + 273 = 323$ K
$V_2 = T_2V_1/T_1 = 323 \times 0.2/523 = 0.123$ m³

---

## 1.4.5 Boyle's law

If we keep the temperature constant and increase the volume, then the molecules will hit the surface less often so the pressure goes down. This gives us Boyle's law:

$p = c/V$   or   $pV = c$   **when $T$ is constant**

---

**WORKED EXAMPLE 1.4**

A mass of gas has a pressure of 800 kPa and volume of 0.3 m³. The pressure is changed to 100 kPa but the temperature is unchanged. Determine the new volume.

*Solution*
Using Boyle's law we find

$$p_1V_1 = c = p_2V_2$$

where   $p_1 = 800 \times 10^3$      $V_1 = 0.3$      $p_2 = 100 \times 10^3$
$V_2 = p_1V_1/p_2 = [(800 \times 10^3) \times 0.3]/(100 \times 10^3)$
$= 2.4$ m³

---

## 1.4.6 General gas law

Consider a gas that undergoes a change in $p$, $V$ and $T$ from point 1 to point 2. It could have gone from 1 to A and then from A to 2 as shown in Fig. 1.6.

**Fig. 1.6**  *Gas expansion by two routes*

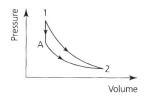

Process 1 to A is constant volume, so $\quad \dfrac{p_A}{T_A} = \dfrac{p_1}{T_1}$

Process A to 2 is constant temperature, so $\quad T_2 = T_A$

Substituting:

$$\frac{p_A}{T_2} = \frac{p_1}{T_1} \quad \text{and} \quad p_A = \frac{p_1 T_2}{T_1} \tag{1.1}$$

For the process A to 2 Boyle's law applies, so $\quad p_A V_A = p_2 V_2$

Since $V_A = V_1$ we can write $\quad p_A V_1 = p_2 V_2$

Rearranging:

$$p_A = \frac{p_2 V_2}{V_1} \tag{1.2}$$

Equating (1.1) and (1.2) we get $\quad \dfrac{p_1 T_2}{T_1} = \dfrac{p_2 V_2}{V_1}$

Rearranging:

$$\frac{p_1 V_1}{T_1} = \frac{p_2 V_2}{T_2}$$

This is the **general gas law** and it is used to calculate one unknown when a gas changes from one condition to another.

---

**WORKED EXAMPLE 1.5**

A mass of gas has a pressure of 1.2 MPa, a volume of 0.03 m³ and a temperature of 100 °C. If the pressure is changed to 400 kPa and the volume is changed to 0.06 m³, determine the new temperature.

*Solution*

Using the general gas law, we find

$\quad p_1 V_1 / T_1 = p_2 V_2 / T_2$

where $\quad p_1 = 1.2 \times 10^6$ N/m²

$\qquad\quad V_1 = 0.03$ m³

$\qquad\quad V_2 = 0.06$ m³

$\qquad\quad p_2 = 400 \times 10^3$ N/m²

$\qquad\quad T_1 = 100 + 273 = 373$ K

$$T_2 = \frac{p_2 V_2 T_1}{p_1 V_1} = \frac{(400 \times 10^3) \times 0.06 \times 373}{(1.2 \times 10^6) \times 0.03} = 248.7 \text{ K}$$

### 1.4.7 Characteristic gas law

The general gas law tells us that when a gas changes from one pressure, volume and temperature to another, then

$$\frac{pV}{T} = \text{constant}$$

If we again consider the gas in the rigid vessel and double the number of molecules – but keep the volume and temperature the same – there would be twice as many impacts with the surface and hence twice the pressure. To keep the pressure the same, the volume would have to be doubled or the temperature halved. It follows that the constant must contain the mass of the gas in order to reflect the number of molecules. The gas law can then be written as

$$\frac{pV}{T} = mR$$

where $m$ is the mass in kg and $R$ is the remaining constant which must be unique for each gas and is called the **characteristic gas constant**.

If we examine the units of $R$ they are J/kg K.

The equation is usually written as $\qquad\qquad pV = mRT$

Since $m/V$ is the density $\rho$, it follows that $\qquad \rho = p/RT$

Since $V/m$ is the specific volume $v$, then $\qquad v = RT/p$

---

**WORKED EXAMPLE 1.6**

A mass of gas has a pressure of 1.2 MPa, a volume of 0.03 m³ and a temperature of 100 °C. Given that the characteristic gas constant is 300 J/kg K, find the mass.

*Solution*

$$m = \frac{pV}{RT} = \frac{(1.2 \times 10^6) \times 0.03}{300 \times 373} = 0.3217 \text{ kg}$$

---

### 1.4.8 The universal gas law

The characteristic gas law states that $pV = mRT$, where $R$ is the characteristic constant for the gas. This law can be made universal for any gas because $R = R_0/M_m$, where $M_m$ is the mean molecular mass of the gas (numerically equal to the relative molecular mass). The formula becomes:

$$pV = mR_0T/M_m$$

$R_0$ is a universal constant with a value of 8314.3 J/kmol K.

The kilomole is defined as the number of kilograms of substance numerically equal to the mean molecular mass. Typical values are:

| Gas | Symbol | $M_m$ |
|---|---|---|
| Hydrogen | $H_2$ | 2 |
| Oxygen | $O_2$ | 32 |
| Carbon dioxide | $CO_2$ | 44 |
| Methane | $CH_4$ | 16 |
| Nitrogen | $N_2$ | 28 |
| Dry air | | 28.96 |

hence:  1 kmol of hydrogen ($H_2$) is 2 kg
1 kmol of oxygen ($O_2$) is 32 kg
1 kmol of nitrogen is 28 kg, and so on.

For example, if you had 3 kmol of nitrogen ($N_2$) you would have

$3 \times 28 = 84$ kg

It follows that $M_m$ must have units of kg/kmol. In order to calculate the characteristic gas constant we use

$R = R_0/M_m$

For example, the characteristic gas constant for air is

$R = 8314.3/28.96 = 287$

Examine the units

$R = R_0/M_m$     (J/kmol K)/(kg/kmol) = J/kg K

---

## WORKED EXAMPLE 1.7

A vessel contains 0.2 m³ of methane at 60 °C and 500 kPa pressure. Calculate the mass of methane.

**Solution**

$pV = mR_0T/M_m$     $(M_m = 16)$

$$500\,000 \times 0.2 = \frac{m \times 8314.3 \times (273 + 60)}{16}$$

hence:   $m = 0.578$ kg

---

## SELF-ASSESSMENT EXERCISE 1.2

All pressures are absolute. The characteristic gas constant $R$ is 287 J/kg K throughout.

1. Calculate the density of air at 1.013 bar and 15 °C.

2. Air in a vessel has a pressure of 25 bar, a volume of 0.2 m³ and a temperature of 20 °C. It is connected to another empty vessel so that the volume increases to 0.5 m³ but the temperature stays the same. Calculate:

(a) The final pressure
(b) The final density.

3. 1 dm³ of air at 20 °C is heated at a constant pressure of 300 kPa until the volume is doubled. Calculate:
(a) The final temperature
(b) The mass.

4. Air is heated from 20 °C and 400 kPa in a fixed volume of 1 m³. The final pressure is 900 kPa. Calculate:
(a) The final temperature
(b) The mass.

5. 1.2 dm³ of gas is compressed from 1 bar and 20 °C to 7 bar and 90 °C. Calculate:
(a) The new volume
(b) The mass.

6. A gas compressor draws in 0.5 m³/min of nitrogen at 10 °C and 100 kPa pressure. Calculate the mass flow rate.

7. A vessel contains 0.5 m³ of oxygen at 40 °C and 10 bar pressure. Calculate the mass.

## 1.5 Specific heat capacities

On completion of Section 1.5, you should understand the specific heats of gases, the relationship between them and the characteristic gas constant. In this section you will:

- Learn how to calculate the change in internal energy of gases and liquids.
- Learn how to calculate the change in enthalpy of gases and liquids.
- Define the specific heats of fluids.
- Relate specific heat capacities to the characteristic gas constant.

### 1.5.1 *The principal specific heat capacities*

The specific heat capacity of a fluid is defined in two principal ways as follows:

**Constant volume $c_v$**

The specific heat that relates change in specific internal energy $u$ and change in temperature $T$ is defined as:

$$c_v = du/dT$$

If the value of the specific heat capacity $c_v$ is constant over a temperature range $\Delta T$, then we may go from the differential form to the finite form:

$$c_v = \Delta u/\Delta T \text{ J/kg K} \quad \text{hence} \quad \Delta u = c_v \, \Delta T \text{ J/kg K}$$

and for a mass $m$ kg the change is

$$\Delta U = m c_v \, \Delta T \text{ joules}$$

This law indicates that the internal energy of a gas is dependent only on its temperature. This was first stated by Joule and is called **Joule's law**.

### Constant pressure $c_p$

The specific heat that relates change in specific enthalpy $h$ and change in temperature $T$ is defined as:

$$c_p = \mathrm{d}h/\mathrm{d}T.$$

If the value of the specific heat capacity $c_p$ is constant over a temperature range $\Delta T$ then we may go from the differential form to the finite form

$$c_p = \Delta h / \Delta T \text{ J/kg} \quad \text{hence} \quad \Delta h = c_p \, \Delta T \text{ J/kg,}$$

and for a mass $m$ kg the change is

$$\Delta H = m c_p \, \Delta T \text{ joules}$$

The reasons why the two specific heats are given the symbols $c_v$ and $c_p$ will be explained next. They are called the **principal specific heats**.

## 1.5.2 *Constant volume heating*

**Fig. 1.7**  *Heat transfer at constant volume*

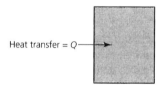

Heat transfer = $Q$

When a fluid is heated at constant volume, the heat transfer $Q$ (Fig. 1.7) must be the same as the increase in internal energy of the fluid $\Delta U$ since no other energy is involved. It follows that

$$Q = \Delta U = m c_v \, \Delta T \text{ joules}$$

The change in internal energy is the same as the heat transfer at constant volume so the specific heat $c_v$ should be remembered as applying to constant volume processes as well as internal energy.

## 1.5.3 *Constant pressure heating*

When a fluid is heated at constant pressure, the volume must increase against a surrounding pressure equal and opposite to the fluid pressure $p$ (Fig. 1.8). The force exerted on the surroundings must be

$$F = pA \text{ newton}$$

**Fig. 1.8** *Heat transfer at constant pressure*

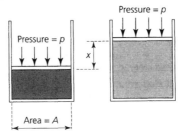

The work done is:

$$W = Fx = pAx = p\,\Delta V,$$

where $\Delta V$ is the volume change.

The heat transfer $Q$ must be equal to the increase in internal energy plus the work done against the external pressure. The work done has the same formula as flow energy, $p\,\Delta V$.

Enthalpy was defined as $\Delta H = \Delta U + p\,\Delta V$. The heat transfer at constant pressure is also

$$Q = \Delta U + p\,\Delta V$$

Since specific heats are used to calculate heat transfers, then in this case the heat transfer is, by definition, $Q = mc_p\,\Delta T$, and it follows that

$$\Delta H = Q = mc_p\,\Delta T$$

For the same temperature change $\Delta T$ it follows that the heat transfer at constant pressure must be larger than that at constant volume. The specific heat capacity, $c_p$, is remembered as being linked to constant pressure.

### 1.5.4 *The relationship between the principal specific heats and the characteristic gas constant*

The enthalpy change at constant pressure is given by

$$\Delta H = mc_p\,\Delta T = \Delta U + p\,\Delta V$$

We have already defined $\Delta U = mc_v\,\Delta T$. Furthermore, for a gas only, $p\,\Delta V = mR\,\Delta T$, therefore:

$$mc_p\,\Delta T = mc_v\,\Delta T + mR\,\Delta T$$
$$\text{hence} \quad c_p = c_v + R$$

### 1.5.5 *Specific heat capacities of liquids*

Since the volume of a liquid changes only slightly when heated or cooled, very little work is done against the surrounding pressure. For all intents and purposes $c_v$ and $c_p$ are the same, and the heat transfer to a liquid is usually given as

$$Q = mc \, \Delta T$$

where $c$ is the specific heat capacity.

## 1.5.6 *Vapours*

A vapour is defined as a gaseous substance close to the temperature at which it will condense back into a liquid. In this state it cannot be considered as a perfect gas and great care should be taken when applying specific heats to vapours. We should use tables and charts to determine the properties of vapours and this is discussed in the next section.

---

### WORKED EXAMPLE 1.8

Calculate the change in enthalpy and internal energy when 3 kg of gas is heated from 20 °C to 200 °C. The specific heat at constant pressure is 1.2 kJ/kg K and at constant volume it is 0.8 kJ/kg K. Also determine the change in flow energy.

*Solution*

(a)  Change in enthalpy:        $\Delta H = mc_p \, \Delta T = 3 \times 1.2 \times 180 = 648$ kJ
(b)  Change in internal energy:   $\Delta U = mc_v \, \Delta T = 3 \times 0.8 \times 180 = 432$ kJ
(c)  Change in flow energy:       $\Delta FE = \Delta H - \Delta U = 216$ kJ

---

### WORKED EXAMPLE 1.9

A vertical cylinder contains 2 dm$^3$ of air at 50 °C. One end of the cylinder is closed and the other end has a frictionless piston which may move under the action of weights placed on it. The weight of the piston and load is 300 N. The cylinder has a cross-sectional area of 0.015 m$^2$. The outside is at atmospheric conditions. Determine:

1.  The gas pressure.
2.  The gas mass.
3.  The distance moved by the piston when the gas is heated to 150 °C.

For air take $c_p = 1005$ J/kg K and $c_v = 718$ J/kg K.
Atmospheric pressure = 100 kPa

*Solution*
The pressure of the gas is constant and always just sufficient to support the piston, therefore:

$p$ = weight/area + atmospheric pressure
    = 300/0.015 + 100 kPa = 20 kPa + 100 kPa = 120 kPa

$T_1 = 50 + 273 = 323$ K
$V_1 = 0.002$ m$^3$
$R = c_p - c_v = 1005 - 718 = 287$ J/kg K

Hence: $m = \dfrac{pV}{RT} = \dfrac{120\,000 \times 0.002}{287 \times 323} = 0.00259$ kg

$T_2 = 150 + 273 = 423$ K

$V_2 = \dfrac{p_1 V_1 T_2}{p_2 T_1}$ but $p_1 = p_2$, therefore:

$V_2 = \dfrac{V_1 T_2}{T_1} = \dfrac{0.002 \times 423}{323} = 0.00262$ m$^3$

hence: Distance moved $= \dfrac{\text{volume change}}{\text{area}} = \dfrac{0.00262 - 0.002}{0.015} = 0.0412$ m

## SELF-ASSESSMENT EXERCISE 1.3

For air take $c_p = 1005$ J/kg K and $c_v = 718$ J/kg K unless otherwise stated.

1. 0.2 kg of air is heated at constant volume from 40 °C to 120 °C. Calculate the heat transfer and change in internal energy.

2. 0.5 kg of air is cooled from 200 °C to 80 °C at a constant pressure of 5 bar. Calculate the change in internal energy, the heat transfer and change in flow energy.

3. 32 kg/s of water is heated from 15 °C to 80 °C. Calculate the heat transfer rate, given $c = 4186$ J/kg K.

4. Air is heated from 20 °C to 50 °C at constant pressure. Using your fluid tables determine the average value of $c_p$ and calculate the heat transfer per kg of air.

5. Figure 1.9 shows a cylinder fitted with a frictionless piston. The air inside is heated to 200 °C at constant pressure causing the piston to rise. Atmospheric pressure outside is 100 kPa. Determine:
   (a) The mass of air.
   (b) The change in internal energy.
   (c) The change in enthalpy.
   (d) The pressure throughout.
   (e) The change in volume.

**Fig. 1.9** *Cylinder fitted with a frictionless piston*

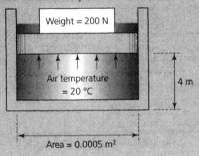

Weight = 200 N

Air temperature = 20 °C

4 m

Area = 0.0005 m²

You should now be able to determine the properties of gases. Next, we will examine the properties of liquids and vapours.

# 1.6 Properties of liquids and vapours

When you have completed this section you should be able to:

- Use tables and charts to find the properties of vapours and liquids.
- Explain dry, wet and superheated vapour.

You should ensure that you have a copy of *Thermodynamic and Transport Properties of Fluids* by Mayhew and Rogers.

## 1.6.1 *General theory*

When a liquid changes into a vapour by the process of evaporation, it undergoes a change of state or phase. The reverse process is called *liquefaction* or *condensing*. The following work should lead you to an understanding of this process. On completion, you should be able to find the same quantities and do the same types of problem that you have already done for gas.

When a liquid is heated, the temperature rises in direct proportion to the heat transferred, $Q$. This is given by $Q = mc \, \Delta T$. The specific heat $c$ is reasonably constant but alters significantly if the pressure or temperature change is very large. If you require the enthalpy of high-pressure water, consult Table 1.1.

When discussing heat transfer and energy of a fluid, we may wish to consider the internal energy $U$ or the enthalpy $H$. In the following, the energy of the fluid may be construed as either $U$ or $H$. In tables this is tabulated as specific internal energy or enthalpy $u$ and $h$.

**Table 1.1 *Enthalpy of high-pressure water***

| Temperature (°C) | Pressure (BARS) | | | | | | | | | | |
|---|---|---|---|---|---|---|---|---|---|---|---|
| | 0 | 25 | 50 | 75 | 100 | 125 | 150 | 175 | 200 | 221 | 250 |
| 0 | 0 | 2.5 | 5 | 7.5 | 10 | 12.6 | 15 | 17.5 | 20 | 22 | 25 |
| 20 | 84 | 86 | 87 | 91 | 93 | 96 | 98 | 100 | 103 | 105 | 107 |
| 40 | 168 | 170 | 172 | 174 | 176 | 179 | 181 | 183 | 185 | 187 | 190 |
| 60 | 251 | 253 | 255 | 257 | 259 | 262 | 264 | 266 | 268 | 270 | 272 |
| 80 | 335 | 337 | 339 | 341 | 343 | 345 | 347 | 349 | 351 | 352 | 355 |
| 100 | 419 | 421 | 423 | 425 | 427 | 428 | 430 | 432 | 434 | 436 | 439 |
| 120 | 504 | 505 | 507 | 509 | 511 | 512 | 514 | 516 | 518 | 519 | 521 |
| 140 | 589 | 591 | 592 | 594 | 595 | 597 | 599 | 600 | 602 | 603 | 605 |
| 160 | 675 | 677 | 678 | 690 | 681 | 683 | 684 | 686 | 687 | 688 | 690 |
| 180 | 763 | 764 | 765 | 767 | 767 | 769 | 770 | 772 | 773 | 774 | 776 |
| 200 | 852 | 853 | 854 | 856 | 856 | 857 | 858 | 859 | 861 | 862 | 863 |

When the liquid receives enough heat to bring it to boiling point, the energy it contains is called **sensible energy**. In tables this is denoted as $u_f$ or $h_f$.

A liquid starts to evaporate because it becomes saturated with heat and can absorb no more without changing state (into a vapour and hence a gas). For this reason, the boiling point is more correctly described as the **saturation temperature**, and the liquid in this state is called **saturated liquid**. The saturation temperature is denoted as $t_s$ in tables.

If a boiling liquid is supplied with more heat, it will evaporate and vapour is driven off. The vapour is still at the saturation temperature and is called **dry saturated vapour**.

A vapour is a gas near to the temperature at which it will condense.

In order to convert liquid into vapour, extra heat must be transferred into it. The amount of enthalpy and internal energy required to evaporate 1 kg are denoted $h_{fg}$ and $u_{fg}$ in tables, and these are called the **latent enthalpy** and **latent internal energy** respectively.

The energy contained in 1 kg of dry saturated vapour must be the sum of the sensible and latent energies, and this is denoted $h_g$ and $u_g$. It follows that:

$$h_g = h_f + h_{fg} \quad \text{and} \quad u_g = u_f + u_{fg}$$

The temperature at which evaporation occurs, $t_s$, depends upon the pressure at which it takes place. For example, we all know that water boils at 100 °C at atmospheric pressure (1.013 bar). At pressures below this, the boiling point is lower; at pressures above this the boiling point is higher. If we look up the values of $t_s$ and $p$ for water in the tables and plot them we get the graph shown in Fig. 1.10. It should also be noted that if the temperature of a liquid is kept constant, it may be made to boil by changing the pressure. The pressure at which it boils is called the **saturation pressure** and is denoted as $p_s$ in the tables.

Figure 1.10 also shows the freezing point of water plotted against pressure (pressure has little effect on it).

The graphs in Fig. 1.10 cross at 0.01 °C and 0.006112 bar. This point is called the **triple point** (T). The graph shows the three phases of ice, water and steam. At the triple

**Fig. 1.10**  *Relationship between the pressure, saturation temperature and freezing temperature of water*

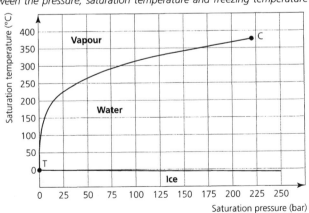

point, all three can occur together. Below the triple point, ice can change into steam without a liquid stage (and vice versa). All substances have a triple point.

If you plotted a graph of $t_s$ against $p$ for water/steam, you would find that the tables stop at 221.2 bar and 374.15 °C. Above this pressure and temperature, the phenomenon of evaporation does not occur and no latent energy stage exists. This point is called the **critical point** (C), and every substance has one.

If vapour is heated, it becomes hotter than the boiling point, and the more it is heated the more it becomes a gas. Such vapour is referred to as **superheated vapour**, except when it is a substance at pressures and temperatures above the critical point, when it is called **supercritical vapour**.

## 1.6.2 *Continuous evaporation*

A simple boiler or evaporator (Fig. 1.11) is needed to produce vapour continuously from liquid. The liquid is pumped in at the same rate at which the vapour is driven off. The heat transfer rate needed to do this must supply the internal energy to the process and the flow energy. In other words, the heat transfer is equal to the increase in the enthalpy from liquid to vapour. This is why enthalpy is such an important property.

**Fig. 1.11**  *Continuous evaporation in a boiler*

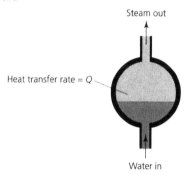

Steam out

Heat transfer rate = $Q$

Water in

## 1.6.3 *Wet vapour*

Wet vapour is a mixture of dry saturated vapour and liquid droplets. It may also be thought of as a partially evaporated substance. In order to understand its properties, consider the evaporation of 1 kg of water, which is illustrated by the temperature–enthalpy graph shown in Fig. 1.12.

Starting with water at atmospheric pressure and 0.01 °C, the enthalpy is arbitrarily taken as zero. When the pressure remains constant and the temperature is raised, the enthalpy of the water rises to 419.1 kJ/kg at 100 °C. At this point it is saturated water and the sensible enthalpy is $h_f = 419.1$ kJ/kg.

The addition of further heat will cause the water to evaporate. During evaporation, the temperature remains at 100 °C. When the latent enthalpy, $h_{fg}$ (= 2256.7 kJ/kg) has been added, the substance is dry saturated vapour and its specific enthalpy $h_g$ is

**Fig. 1.12** *Relationship between temperature and enthalpy of water/steam at atmospheric pressure*

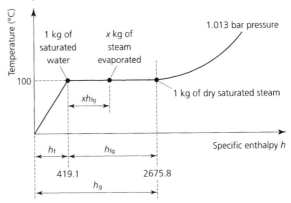

2675.8 kJ/kg. Further addition of heat will cause the temperature to rise and the substance becomes superheated vapour.

A graph similar to that in Fig. 1.12 may be drawn for any pressure, and the same basic shape will be obtained but of course with different values. At the critical pressure it will be found that $h_{fg}$ is zero.

The point of interest is the enthalpy value at some point along the evaporation line. Any point on this line represents wet steam. Suppose only fraction, $x$ kg, has been evaporated. The latent enthalpy added will only be $xh_{fg}$ and not $h_{fg}$. The enthalpy of the water/steam mixture is then

$$h = h_f + xh_{fg}$$

The fraction $x$ is called the **dryness fraction**. It is, however, rarely given as a fraction and usually as a decimal. If no evaporation has started, then $x = 0$; if all the liquid is evaporated, then $x = 1$. ($x$ cannot be larger than 1 as this would mean that the vapour is superheated.)

The same logic applies to internal energy, and it follows that

$$u = u_f + xu_{fg}$$

### 1.6.4 *Volumes*

The specific volume of saturated water is denoted by $v_f$. The specific volume of dry saturated steam is denoted by $v_g$. The change in volume from water to steam is $v_{fg}$. It follows that the specific volume of wet steam is

$$v = v_f + xv_{fg}$$

Since the value of $v_f$ is very small and the specific volume of dry steam is very large (in all but the extreme cases), then $v_{fg}$ is practically the same as $v_g$ and $v_f$ is negligible.

The specific volume of steam is then usually calculated from the formula

$$v = xv_g$$

### 1.6.5 *Total values*

All the formulas shown represent the values for 1 kg (specific values). When the mass is $m$ kg, the values are simply multiplied by $m$. For example, the volume of $m$ kg of wet steam becomes $V = mxv_g$.

### 1.6.6 *Saturation curve*

If we plot a graph of $h_f$ and $h_g$ against either temperature or pressure, we get a property chart. The graph itself is the **saturation curve**. Taking the pressure–enthalpy ($p$–$h$) graph as an example (Fig. 1.13) temperatures and dryness fractions may be drawn on it, and with the resulting graph the enthalpy of water, wet, dry or superheated steam, may be found. The pressure–enthalpy chart is popular for refrigerants but not for steam.

**Fig. 1.13** *Pressure–enthalpy diagram for water/steam*

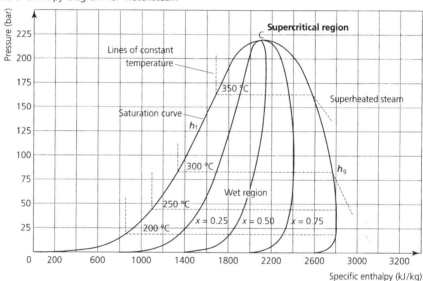

### 1.6.7 *Use of tables*

It is vitally important that you should be able to use the fluid tables in order to find the properties of steam. You must have a copy and become completely proficient in their use. Regarding water/steam, the tables contain a section on saturated water/steam and a section on superheated/supercritical steam.

The saturated water/steam tables are laid out as follows, with an example of values. Check this out for yourself.

| $p$ | $t_s$ | $v_g$ | $u_f$ | $u_g$ | $h_f$ | $h_{fg}$ | $h_g$ | $s_f$ | $s_{fg}$ | $s_g$ |
|---|---|---|---|---|---|---|---|---|---|---|
| 10 | 179.9 | 0.1944 | 762 | 2584 | 763 | 2015 | 2778 | 2.138 | 4.448 | 6.586 |

The columns headed $s$ are entropy values that have not yet been explained.

The latent internal energy $u_{fg}$ is not listed because of lack of room. However, you do need to remember that it is the difference between $u_f$ and $u_g$. Note that in all cases the value of $h_{fg}$ is the difference between the values on either side of it.

The superheat tables are laid out differently and an example is shown in the next worked example. In this case the values depends upon the pressure and temperature since the steam can exist at any pressure and temperature above the saturation values. This, by necessity, makes the tables very concise. Interpolation is required to find values between those tabulated.

In the superheat tables, you must locate the temperature along the top and the pressure down the side. This results in set of values at these coordinates, giving $v$, $u$, $h$ and $s$.

---

**WORKED EXAMPLE 1.10**

Find the specific enthalpy, internal energy and volume of steam at 3 bar and 200 °C.

*Solution*
Locate the column with 200 °C at the top and come down the page to the row with 3 bar at the left side. At this point, you have a block of 4 figures. The enthalpy value is the third figure down and is 2866 kJ/kg. The second figure down is the internal energy and is 2651 kJ/kg. The first figure is the volume and is 0.7166 m³/kg. You don't need the fourth figure at this stage.

| $p$/bar | $t$ | 50 | 100 | 150 | 200 | 250 | |
|---------|-----|-----|-----|-----|-----|-----|---|
| 3 | | | | | 0.7166 | | volume |
| (133.5) | | | | | 2651 | | int. energy |
| | | | | | 2866 | | enthalpy |
| | | | | | 7.312 | | entropy |

---

**WORKED EXAMPLE 1.11**

Find the enthalpy, internal energy and volume of 3 kg of steam at 11 bar and dryness 0.75.

*Solution*
From page 4 of the steam tables determine the row corresponding to 11 bar and look up the following values:

$h_f = 781$ kJ/kg     $h_{fg} = 2000$ kJ/kg     $h_g = 2781$ kJ/kg
$u_f = 780$ kJ/kg     $u_g = 2586$ kJ/kg
$v_g = 0.1774$ m³/kg

Next deduce   $u_{fg} = 2586 - 780 = 1806$ kJ/kg
Now find the enthalpy:

$$H = m(h_f + xh_{fg}) = 3(781 + 0.75 \times 2000) = 6843 \text{ kJ}$$

---

Next find the internal energy in the same way:

$$U = m(u_f + xu_{fg}) = 3(780 + 0.75 \times 1806) = 6403.5 \text{ kJ}$$

Finally, find the volume:

$$V = mxv_g = 3 \times 0.75 \times 0.1774 = 0.399 \text{ m}^3$$

---

**SELF-ASSESSMENT EXERCISE 1.4**

Use tables to answer the following questions.

1. What is the saturation temperature at 32 bar?

2. What is the specific enthalpy and internal energy of saturated water at 16 bar?

3. What is the specific enthalpy and internal energy of dry saturated steam at 16 bar?

4. Subtract the enthalpy in 2 from that in 3 and check that it is the latent enthalpy $h_{fg}$ at 16 bar in the tables.

5. What is the specific enthalpy and internal energy of superheated steam at 10 bar and 400 °C?

6. What is the specific volume of dry saturated steam at 20 bar?

7. What is the volume of 1 kg of wet steam at 20 bar with dryness fraction $x = 0.7$?

8. What is the specific enthalpy and internal energy of wet steam at 20 bar with a dryness fraction of 0.7?

9. What is the specific volume of superheated steam at 15 bar and 500 °C?

10. What is the volume and enthalpy of 3 kg of wet steam at 5 bar with dryness fraction 0.9?

11. What is the enthalpy of 1.5 kg of superheated steam at 8 bar and 350 °C?

12. What is the internal energy of 2.2 kg of dry saturated steam at 11 bar?

13. What is the volume of 0.5 kg of superheated steam at 15 bar and 400 °C?

## 1.7 Entropy

Entropy, which is mentioned throughout this book, is explained in more detail in Chapter 3. As it will be necessary for you to find entropy values of steam, this section is needed for those who are not familiar with it.

The definition of entropy that is most useful to these studies is as follows. *If an infinitesimally small heat transfer dQ occurs at temperature T, there is an infinitesimally small change in entropy dS.*

$$\mathrm{d}Q = T\,\mathrm{d}S$$

Entropy $S$ has units of J/kg K and specific entropy has units of kJ/kg K.

Heat transfer often takes place by transporting entropy in a fluid, so it follows that a fluid may have entropy as a property.

[Those studying the BTEC/Edexcel module need only find the entropy of steam. Those who also need to find the entropy of gases will find Appendix B useful.]

## 1.7.1 *Finding entropy values from vapour tables*

Entropy values for vapours should be found from your thermodynamic tables. You may look up values in the $s$ columns in exactly the same way as you do for enthalpy and internal energy. The suffixes have exactly the same meaning as for other properties, hence:

$s_f$ is the specific entropy for saturated liquid.
$s_g$ is the specific entropy for dry saturated vapour.
$s_{fg}$ is the specific entropy change during evaporation and $s_{fg} = s_g - s_f$.

For superheated and supercritical vapours, look up $s$ values as appropriate. If the heat transfer $Q$ is equal to the change in enthalpy

$$\mathrm{d}s = \mathrm{d}Q/T = (\mathrm{d}h)/T$$

During evaporation at constant pressure, temperature is also constant (the saturation temperature). The change in specific enthalpy is $h_{fg}$ and the change in specific entropy is $s_{fg}$. Since $T = t_s$ (in Kelvin), it follows that

$$\Delta s = h_{fg}/T = s_{fg}$$

The entropy values in your steam tables are based on enthalpy changes.

---

**WORKED EXAMPLE 1.12**

1.  Find the specific entropy of superheated steam at 50 bar and 400 °C.
    From tables, $s = 6.646$ kJ/kg K.
2.  Find the specific entropy of dry saturated steam at 20 bar.
    From tables, $s_g = 6.340$ kJ/kg K.
3.  Find the specific entropy of saturated water at 20 bar.
    From tables, $s_f = 2.447$ kJ/kg K.
4.  Find the specific entropy change during evaporation at 20 bar.
    $\Delta s = s_{fg} = s_g - s_f = 6.340 - 2.447 = 3.893$ kJ/kg K.
    From the tables this could be found direct under the $s_{fg}$ column.

---

## WORKED EXAMPLE 1.13

Find the specific entropy of wet steam at 20 bar with dryness fraction 0.82.

**Solution**
The same rule applies as for other properties:

$$s = s_f + x s_{fg} = 2.447 + (0.82)(3.893) = 5.639 \text{ kJ/kg K}.$$

## SELF-ASSESSMENT EXERCISE 1.5

Find the specific entropy for the following using your tables:

1.  Superheated steam at 10 bar and 500 °C.

2.  Ammonia vapour at 3.983 bar and 98 °C.

3.  Wet steam at 12 bar and 0.9 dry.

4.  Wet steam at 200 bar and 0.95 dry.

5.  Find the change in specific entropy when steam at 200 bar and 0.95 dry changes to 12 bar and 0.9 dry.

# **2** Thermodynamic systems

When you have completed this chapter, you should be able to:

- Explain and use the first law of thermodynamics.
- Solve problems involving various kinds of thermodynamic systems.
- Explain and use polytropic expansion and compression processes.

## 2.1 Energy transfer

When you complete this section you should be able to explain and calculate the following:

- Heat transfer.
- Heat transfer rate.
- Work transfer.
- Work transfer rate (power).

### 2.1.1 *Heat transfer*

Heat transfer occurs because one place is hotter than another. In normal circumstances, heat will only flow from a hot body to a cold body by virtue of the temperature difference. There are three mechanisms for this: *conduction, convection* and *radiation* (Fig. 2.1). You do not need to study the laws governing conduction, convection and radiation in this module.

**Fig. 2.1** *Heat transfer from hot to cold*

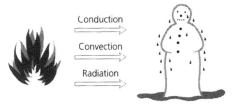

Conduction

Convection

Radiation

A quantity of energy transferred as heat is given the symbol $Q$ and its basic unit is the *joule*. The quantity transferred in one second is the **heat transfer rate**; its symbol is $\Phi$ and its unit is the *watt*.

An example of this is when heat passes from the furnace of a steam boiler through the walls separating the combustion chamber from the water and steam. In this case, conduction, convection and radiation all occur together (Fig. 2.2).

**Fig. 2.2** *Simple boiler design*

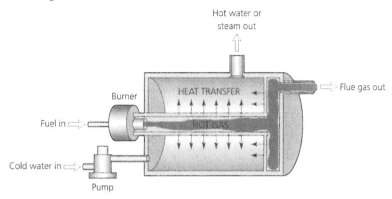

**SELF-ASSESSMENT EXERCISE 2.1**

1. 1 kg/s of steam flows in a pipe 40 mm bore at 200 bar pressure and 400 °C.
   (a) Look up the specific volume of the steam and determine the mean velocity in the pipe.
   (b) Determine the kinetic energy being transported per second.
   (c) Determine the enthalpy being transported per second.

## 2.1.2 *Work transfer*

Energy may be transported from one place to another mechanically, as when the output shaft of a car engine transfers energy to the wheels. A quantity of energy transferred as work is $W$ joules, but the work transferred in one second is the power $P$ watts.

As an example of power transfer, consider the shaft of a steam turbine used to transfer energy from the steam turbine to the generator in an electric power station (Fig. 2.3).

It is useful to remember that the power transmitted by a shaft depends upon the torque and the angular velocity. The formulas used are

$$P = \omega T \quad \text{or} \quad P = 2\pi N T$$

where $\omega$ is the angular velocity in radian per second and $N$ is the angular velocity in revolutions per second.

**Fig. 2.3** *Mechanical power transfer from a turbine to a generator*

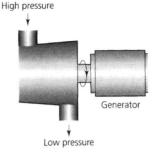

High pressure

Generator

Low pressure

---

**WORKED EXAMPLE 2.1**

A duct has a cross-section of 0.2 m × 0.4 m. Steam flows through it at a rate of 3 kg/s with a pressure of 2 bar. The steam has a dryness fraction of 0.98. Calculate all the individual forms of energy being transported.

***Solution***
Cross-sectional area = 0.2 × 0.4 = 0.08 m²
Volume flow rate = $mxv_g$ at 2 bar
Volume flow rate = 3 × 0.98 × 0.8856 = 2.6 m³/s
Velocity = $c$ = volume/area = 2.6/0.08 = 32.5 m/s
kinetic energy being transported = $mc^2/2$ = 3 × 32.5²/2 = 1584 W
Enthalpy being transported = $m(h_f + xh_{fg})$

$H$ = 3(505 + 0.98 × 2202) = 7988.9 kW

Flow energy being transported = pressure × volume
Flow energy = 2 × 10⁵ × 2.6 = 520 000 W
Internal energy being transported = $m(u_f + xu_{fg})$

$U$ = 3(505 + 0.98 × 2025) = 7468.5 kW

Check flow energy = $H - U$ = 7988.9 - 7468.5 = 520 kW

---

**SELF-ASSESSMENT EXERCISE 2.2**

1. The shaft of a steam turbine produces 600 N m torque at 50 rev/s. Calculate the work transfer rate from the steam.

2. A car engine produces 30 kW of power at 3000 rev/min. Calculate the torque produced.

---

## 2.2 The first law of thermodynamics

When you have completed this section, you should be able to explain and use the following terms:

- The first law of thermodynamics.
- Closed systems.
- The non-flow energy equation.
- Open systems.
- The steady flow energy equation.

### 2.2.1 *Thermodynamic systems*

In order to do energy calculations, we identify our system and draw a boundary around it to separate it from the surroundings (Fig. 2.4). We can then keep account of all the energy crossing the boundary. The first law simply states that

> The net energy transfer = net energy change of the system
> Energy transfer into the system = $E_{in}$
> Energy transfer out of the system = $E_{out}$
> Nett change of energy inside the system = $E_{in} - E_{out} = \Delta E$

This is the fundamental form of the first law.

Thermodynamic systems might contain only static fluid, in which case they are called **non-flow** or **closed systems**. Alternatively, there may be a steady flow of fluid through the system, in which case it is known as a **steady flow** or **open system**.

The energy equation is fundamentally different for each because most energy forms only apply to a fluid in motion. We will look at non-flow systems first.

**Fig. 2.4** *General representation of a thermodynamic system*

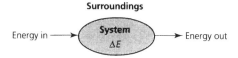

### 2.2.2 *Non-flow systems*

The rules governing non-flow systems are as follows:

- The volume of the boundary may change.
- No fluid crosses the boundary.
- Energy may be transferred across the boundary.

When the volume enlarges, work $(-W)$ is transferred from the system to the surroundings. When the volume shrinks, work $(+W)$ is transferred from the surroundings into the system. Energy may also be transferred into the system as heat $(+Q)$ or out of the system $(-Q)$. This is best shown with the example of a piston sliding inside a cylinder filled with a fluid such as gas (Fig. 2.5).

**Fig. 2.5** *An example of a non-flow system*

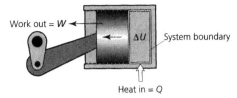

Work out = $W$

$\Delta U$

System boundary

Heat in = $Q$

The only energy possessed by the fluid is internal energy, $U$, so the nett change is $\Delta U$. The energy equation becomes

$$Q + W = \Delta U$$

This is known as the **non-flow energy equation** (NFEE).

### 2.2.3 Steady flow systems

The laws governing this type of system are as follows:

- Fluid enters and leaves through the boundary at a steady rate.
- Energy may be transferred into or out of the system.

A good example of this system is a steam turbine (Fig. 2.6). Energy may be transferred out as a rate of heat transfer $\Phi$ or as a rate of work transfer $P$.

**Fig. 2.6** *An example of a steady-flow system*

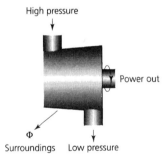

High pressure

Power out

$\Phi$

Surroundings    Low pressure

The fluid entering and leaving has potential energy (PE), kinetic energy (KE) and enthalpy ($H$).

The first law becomes $\Phi + P$ = nett change in energy of the fluid.

$$\Phi + P = \Delta(\text{PE})/s + \Delta(\text{KE})/s + \Delta(H)/s$$

This is called the **steady flow energy equation** (SFEE), and again we will use the convention of positive for energy transferred into the system.

Note that the term $\Delta$ means 'change of', and if the inlet is denoted point 1 and the outlet point 2, the change is the difference between the values at 2 and 1. For example, $\Delta H$ means $(H_2 - H_1)$.

**WORKED EXAMPLE 2.2**

A steam turbine is supplied with 30 kg/s of superheated steam at 80 bar and 400 °C with negligible velocity. The turbine shaft produces 200 kN m of torque at 3000 rev/min. There is a heat loss of 1.2 MW from the casing. Determine the thermal power remaining in the exhaust steam.

*Solution*
Shaft power (SP) is

$$SP = 2\pi NT = 2\pi(3000/60) \times 200\,000$$
$$= 62.831 \times 10^6 \text{ W} = 62.831 \text{ MW}$$

Thermal power supplied = $H$ at 80 bar and 400 °C

$$H = 30(3139) = 94\,170 \text{ kW} = 94.17 \text{ MW}$$

Total energy flow into turbine = 94.17 MW
Energy flow out of turbine = 94.17 MW = SP + loss + exhaust
Thermal power in exhaust = 94.17 − 1.2 − 62.831 = **30.14 MW**

**SELF-ASSESSMENT EXERCISE 2.3**

1. A non-flow system receives 80 kJ of heat transfer and loses 20 kJ as work transfer. What is the change in the internal energy of the fluid?

2. A non-flow system receives 100 kJ of heat transfer and also 40 kJ of work is transferred to it. What is the change in the internal energy of the fluid?

3. A steady flow system receives 500 kW of heat and loses 200 kW of work. What is the net change in the energy of the fluid flowing through it?

4. A steady flow system loses 2 kW of heat also loses 4 kW of work. What is the net change in the energy of the fluid flowing through it?

5. A steady flow system loses 3 kW of heat also loses 20 kW of work. The fluid flows through the system at a steady rate of 70 kg/s. The velocity at inlet is 20 m/s and at outlet it is 10 m/s. The inlet is 20 m above the outlet. Calculate:
   (a) The change in KE per second.
   (b) The change in PE per second.
   (c) The change in $H$ per second.

# 2.3 More examples of thermodynamic systems

When we examine a thermodynamic system, we must first decide whether it is a non-flow or a steady flow system. First, we will look at examples of non-flow systems.

## 2.3.1 *Piston in a cylinder (Fig. 2.7)*

**Fig. 2.7** *Energy transfers in a system with a working piston*

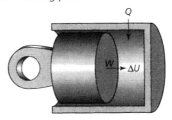

If there is heat and work transfer, the NFEE is

$$Q + W = \Delta U$$

If there is no heat transfer (e.g. when the cylinder is insulated), $Q = 0$ and

$$W = \Delta U$$

If the piston does not move, the volume is fixed and no work transfer occurs. In this case

$$Q = \Delta U$$

For a *gas only* the change in internal energy is $\Delta U = mC_v \, \Delta T$.

## 2.3.2 *Sealed evaporator or condenser*

Since no change in volume occurs, there is no work transfer, so $Q = \Delta U$ (Fig. 2.8).

**Fig. 2.8** *Energy transfer in a sealed evaporator*

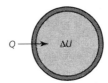

---

**WORKED EXAMPLE 2.3**

30 g of gas inside a cylinder fitted with a piston has a temperature of 15 °C. The piston is moved with a mean force of 200 N so that that it moves 60 mm and compresses the gas. The temperature rises to 21 °C as a result. Calculate the heat transfer, given $c_v = 718$ J/kg K.

---

*Solution*

This is a non-flow system so the law applying is $Q + W = \Delta U$. The change in internal energy is

$$\Delta U = mc_v\,\Delta T = 0.03 \times 718 \times (21 - 15) = 129.24 \text{ J}$$

The work is transferred into the system because the volume shrinks.

$W = \text{force} \times \text{distance moved} = 200 \times 0.06 = 12 \text{ J}$
$Q = \Delta U - W = \mathbf{117.24\ J}$

Now we will look at examples of steady flow systems.

### 2.3.3 *Pumps and fluid motors*

Figure 2.9 shows graphical symbols for hydraulic pumps and motors. The SFEE states,

$$\Phi + P = \Delta KE/s + \Delta PE/s + \Delta H/s$$

In this case, especially if the fluid is a liquid, the velocity is the same at inlet and outlet and the kinetic energy is ignored. If the inlet and outlet are at the same height, the PE is also neglected. Heat transfer does not usually occur in pumps and motors so $\Phi$ is zero.

**Fig. 2.9** *Symbolic representation of a hydraulic pump and motor*

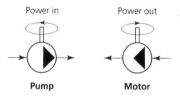

The SFEE simplifies to

$P = \Delta H/s$

Remember that enthalpy is the sum of internal energy and flow energy; therefore the enthalpy of gases, vapours and liquids may be found. In the case of liquids, the change of internal energy is small and so the change in enthalpy is equal to the change in flow energy (FE) only.

The equation simplifies further to $P = \Delta FE/s$. Since $FE = pV$ and $V$ is constant for a liquid, this becomes

$P = V\,\Delta p$

## WORKED EXAMPLE 2.4

A pump delivers 20 kg/s of oil of density 780 kg/m$^3$ from atmospheric pressure at inlet to 800 kPa gauge pressure at outlet. The inlet and outlet pipes are the same size and at the same level. Calculate the theoretical power input.

### Solution

Since the pipes are the same size, the velocities are equal and the change in kinetic energy is zero. Since they are at the same level, the change in potential energy is also zero. (Neglect heat transfer and internal energy.)

$P = V \, \Delta p$
$V = m/\rho = 20/780 = 0.0256$ m$^3$/s
$\Delta p = 800 - 0 = 800$ kPa
**$P = 0.0256 \times 800\,000 = 20\,480$ W or 20.48 kW**

## WORKED EXAMPLE 2.5

A feed pump on a power station pumps 20 kg/s of water. At inlet the water is at 2 bar and 120 °C. At outlet it is at 200 bar and 140 °C. Assuming that there is no heat transfer and that PE and KE are negligible, calculate the theoretical power input.

### Solution

In this case the internal energy has increased due to frictional heating. The SFEE reduces to

$P = \Delta H/s = m(h_2 - h_1)$

The $h$ values may be found from tables:

$h_1 = 504$ kJ/kg

This is near enough the value of $h_f$ at 120 °C in steam tables.

$h_2 = 602$ kJ/kg

**$P = 20(602 - 504) = 1969$ kW or 1.969 MW**

If water tables are not available the problem may be solved as follows:

$\Delta h = \Delta u + \Delta$FE
$\Delta u = c \, \Delta T$, where $c = 4.18$ kJ/kg K for water
$\Delta u = 4.18(140 - 120) = 83.6$ kJ/kg
$\Delta$FE $= V \, \Delta p$

The volume of water is normally around 0.001 m$^3$/kg.

$\Delta$FE $= 0.001 \times (200 - 2) \times 10^5 = 19\,800$ J/kg or 19.8 kJ/kg

hence:   $\Delta h = \Delta u + \Delta$FE $= 83.6 + 19.8 = 103.4$ kJ/kg

**$P = m \, \Delta h = 20 \times 103.4 = 2068$ kW or 2.07 MW**

The discrepancies between the answers are slight and due to the fact the value of the specific heat and of the specific volume are not accurate at 200 bar.

### 2.3.4 *Gas compressors and turbines*

Figure 2.10 shows the basic construction of an axial flow compressor and turbine. These have rows of aerofoil blades on the rotor and in the casing. The turbine passes high-pressure hot gas or steam from left to right making the rotor rotate. The compressor draws in gas and compresses it in stages.

**Fig. 2.10**  *Steady flow compressor and turbine*

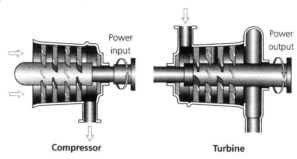

Compressing a gas normally makes it hotter but expanding it makes it colder. This is because gas is compressible and, unlike the cases for liquids already covered, the volumes change dramatically with pressure. This might cause a change in velocity and hence kinetic energy. Both kinetic and potential energy are often negligible, however the internal energy change is not negligible. Figure 2.11 shows graphical symbols for turbines and compressors. Note that the narrow end is always the high-pressure end.

**Fig. 2.11**  *Symbolic representation of steady flow compressor and turbine*

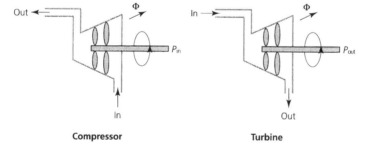

---

### WORKED EXAMPLE 2.6

A gas turbine uses 5 kg/s of hot air. It takes it in at 6 bar and 900 °C and exhausts it at 450 °C. The turbine loses 20 kW of heat from the casing. Calculate the theoretical power output given that $c_p = 1005$ J/kg K.

*Solution*

First identify this as a steady flow system for which the equation is

$$\Phi + P = \Delta KE/s + \Delta PE/s + \Delta H/s$$

For lack of further information we assume KE and PE to be negligible. The heat transfer rate is −20 kW. The enthalpy change for a gas is

$$\Delta H = mC_p \Delta T = 5 \times 1005 \times (450 - 900)$$
$$= -2\ 261\ 000 \text{ W or } -2.261 \text{ MW}$$

$$\boldsymbol{P = \Delta H - \Phi = -2261 - (-20) = -2241 \text{ kW}}$$

The minus sign indicates that the power is leaving the turbine. Note that if this was a steam turbine, you would look up the $h$ values in the steam tables.

### 2.3.5 *Steady flow evaporators and condensers*

A refrigerator is a good example of a thermodynamic system. In particular, it contains a heat exchanger that absorbs heat at a cold temperature and evaporates the liquid into a gas. The gas is compressed and becomes hot; it is then cooled and condensed on the outside of the fridge in another heat exchanger.

**Fig. 2.12** *Basic refrigeration system showing a compressor, evaporator, throttle and condenser*

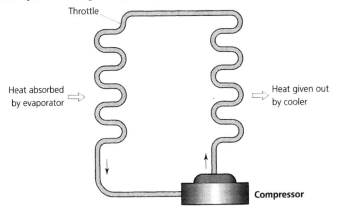

For both the evaporator and condenser, no work is transferred in or out. KE and PE are not normally a feature of such systems, so the SFEE reduces to

$$\Phi = \Delta H / s$$

On steam power plant, boilers are used to raise steam, and these are examples of large evaporators working at high pressures and temperatures. Steam condensers are also found on power stations. The energy equation is the same, whatever the application.

## WORKED EXAMPLE 2.7

A steam condenser takes in wet steam at 8 kg/s and dryness fraction 0.82. This is condensed into saturated water at outlet. The working pressure is 0.05 bar. Calculate the heat transfer rate.

*Solution*

$$\Phi = \Delta H/s = m(h_2 - h_1)$$
$$h_1 = h_f + xh_{fg} \text{ at 0.05 bar}$$

From the steam tables we find that

$$h_1 = 138 + 0.82(2423) = 2125 \text{ kJ/kg}$$
$$h_2 = h_f \text{ at 0.05 bar} = 138 \text{ kJ/kg}$$

Hence: $\Phi = 8(138 - 2125) = -15\ 896 \text{ kW}$

The negative sign indicates heat transferred from the system to the surroundings.

## SELF-ASSESSMENT EXERCISE 2.4

1. Gas is contained inside a cylinder fitted with a piston. The gas is at 20 °C and has a mass of 20 g. The gas is compressed with a mean force of 80 N which moves the piston 50 mm. At the same time 5 J of heat transfer occurs out of the gas. Calculate:
   (a) The work done.
   (b) The change in internal energy.
   (c) The final temperature.
   Take $c_v$ as 718 J/kg K.

2. A steady flow air compressor draws in air at 20 °C and compresses it to 120 °C at outlet. The mass flow rate is 0.7 kg/s. At the same time, 5 kW of heat is transferred into the system. Calculate:
   (a) The change in enthalpy per second.
   (b) The work transfer rate.
   Take $c_p$ as 1005 J/kg K.

3. A steady flow boiler is supplied with water at 15 kg/s, 100 bar pressure and 200 °C. The water is heated and turned into steam. This leaves at 15 kg/s, 100 bar and 500 °C. Using your steam tables, find:
   (a) The specific enthalpy of the water entering.
   (b) The specific enthalpy of the steam leaving.
   (c) The heat transfer rate.

4. A pump delivers 50 dm³/min of water from an inlet pressure of 100 kPa to an outlet pressure of 3 MPa. There is no measurable rise in temperature. Ignoring KE and PE, calculate the work transfer rate.

5. A water pump delivers 130 dm³/min (0.13 m³/min) drawing it in at 100 kPa and delivering it at 500 kPa. Assuming that only flow energy changes occur, calculate the power supplied to the pump.

6. A steam condenser is supplied with 2 kg/s of steam at 0.07 bar and dryness fraction 0.9. The steam is condensed into saturated water at outlet. Determine:
   (a) The specific enthalpies at inlet and outlet.
   (b) The heat transfer rate.

7. 0.2 kg/s of gas is heated at constant pressure in a steady flow system from 10 °C to 180 °C. Calculate the heat transfer rate $\Phi$. ($c_p = 1.1$ kJ/kg K.)

8. 0.3 kg of gas is cooled from 120 °C to 50 °C at constant volume in a closed system. Calculate the heat transfer. ($c_v = 0.8$ kJ/kg K.)

# 2.4 Polytropic processes

When you complete this section you should be able to:

- Use the laws governing the expansion and compression of a fluid.
- State the names of standard processes.
- Derive and use the work laws for closed system expansions and compressions.
- Solve problems involving gas and vapour processes in closed systems.

We will start by examining compression and expansion processes.

## 2.4.1 Compression and expansion processes

A compressible fluid (gas or vapour) may be *compressed* by reducing its volume or *expanded* by increasing its volume. This may be done inside a cylinder by moving a piston or by allowing the pressure to change as it flows through a system such as a turbine. For ease of understanding, let us consider the change as occurring inside a cylinder. The process is best explained with a pressure–volume graph.

When the volume changes, the pressure and temperature may also change. The resulting pressure depends upon the final temperature, and the final temperature depends on whether the fluid is cooled or heated during the process. It is normal to show these changes on a graph of pressure plotted against volume ($p$–$V$ graph). A typical graph for a compression and expansion process is shown in Fig. 2.13.

It has been discovered that the resulting curves follow the mathematical law

$pV^n$ = constant

Depending on whether the fluid is heated or cooled, a family of such curves is obtained, as shown (Fig. 2.14). Each graph has a different value of $n$, which is called the index of expansion or compression. The most common processes are given below.

**Fig. 2.13** *Representation of an expansion and a compression process on a pressure–volume diagram*

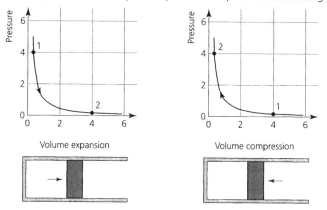

**Fig. 2.14** *Polytropic expansions and compressions*

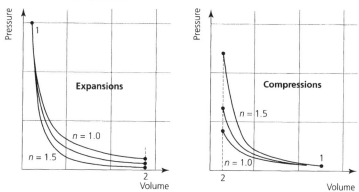

### Constant volume, *also known as* isochoric
A vertical graph is a constant volume process and so it is neither a compression nor an expansion. Since no movement of the piston occurs, no work transfer will take place. Nevertheless, it still fits the law with $n$ having a value of infinity.

### Constant pressure, *also known as* isobaric
A horizontal graph represents a change in volume with no pressure change (constant pressure process). The value of $n$ is zero in this case.

### Constant temperature, *also known as* isothermal
All the graphs between constant volume and constant pressure represent processes with a value of $n$ between infinity and zero. One of these represents the case when the temperature is maintained constant by cooling or heating by just the right amount.

When the fluid is a gas, the law coincides with Boyle's law $pV = \text{constant}$ so it follows that $n$ is 1.

When the fluid is a vapour, the gas law is not accurate and the value of $n$ is close to but not equal to 1.

## Adiabatic process

When the pressure and volume change in such a way that no heat is added or lost from the fluid (e.g. by using an insulated cylinder), the process is called adiabatic. This is an important process and is the one that occurs when the change takes place so rapidly that there is no time for heat transfer to occur. This process represents a demarcation between those in which heat flows into the fluid and those in which heat flows out of the fluid. In order to show it is special, the symbol $\gamma$ is used instead of $n$ and the law is

$$pV^\gamma = C$$

It will be found that each gas has a special value for $\gamma$ (e.g. 1.4 for dry air).

## Polytropic process

All the other curves represent changes with some degree of heat transfer either into or out of the fluid. These are generally known as polytropic processes.

## Hyperbolic process

The process with $n = 1$ is a hyperbola so it is called a hyperbolic process. This is also isothermal for gas but not for vapour. It is usually used in the context of a steam expansion.

---

### WORKED EXAMPLE 2.8

A gas is compressed from 1 bar and 100 cm$^3$ to 20 cm$^3$ by the law $pV^{1.3}$ = constant. Calculate the final pressure.

*Solution*
If $pV^{1.3} = C$ then:

$$p_1 V_1^{1.3} = C = p_2 V_2^{1.3}$$

hence:  $1 \times 100^{1.3} = p_2 \times 20^{1.3}$
$1 \times (100/20)^{1.3} = p_2 = 8.1$ bar

### WORKED EXAMPLE 2.9

Vapour at 10 bar and 30 cm$^3$ is expanded to 1 bar by the law $pV^{1.2} = C$. Find the final volume.

*Solution*

$$p_1 V_1^{1.2} = C = p_2 V_2^{1.2}$$
$10 \times 30^{1.2} = 1 \times V_2^{1.2}$    hence:  $V_2 = (592.3)^{1/1.2} = 204.4$ cm$^3$

---

A gas is compressed from 200 kPa and 120 cm$^3$ to 30 cm$^3$ and the resulting pressure is 1 MPa. Calculate the index of compression $n$.

*Solution*

$200 \times 120^n = 1000 \times 30^n$

$(120/30)^n = 1000/200 = 5$

$4^n = 5$

$n \log 4 = \log 5$

$n = \log 5/\log 4 = 1.6094/1.3863 =$ **1.161**

Note this may be solved with natural or base 10 logs or directly on suitable calculators.

1. A vapour is expanded from 12 bar and 50 cm$^3$ to 150 cm$^3$ and the resulting pressure is 6 bar. Calculate the index of compression $n$.

2. (a) A gas is compressed from 200 kPa and 300 cm$^3$ to 800 kPa by the law $pV^{1.4} = C$. Calculate the new volume.
   (b) The gas was at 50 °C before compression. Calculate the new temperature using the gas law $pV/T = C$.

3. (a) A gas is expanded from 2 MPa and 50 cm$^3$ to 150 cm$^3$ by the law $pV^{1.25} = C$. Calculate the new pressure.
   (b) The temperature was 500 °C before expansion. Calculate the final temperature.

## 2.4.2 *Combining the gas law with the polytropic law*

For gases only, the general law may be combined with the law of expansion as follows:

$$\frac{p_1V_1}{T_1} = \frac{p_2V_2}{T_2} \quad \text{and so} \quad \frac{T_2}{T_1} = \frac{p_2V_2}{p_1V_1}$$

Since for an expansion or compression $p_1V_1^n = p_2V_2^n$:

$$\frac{p_2}{p_1} = \left(\frac{V_1}{V_2}\right)^n$$

Substituting into the gas law we get

$$\frac{T_2}{T_1} = \left(\frac{V_1}{V_2}\right)^{n-1}$$

and further since $(p_1/p_2)^{1/n} = V_2/V_1$, substituting into the gas law gives:

$$\frac{T_2}{T_1} = \left(\frac{p_2}{p_1}\right)^{1-1/n}$$

To summarise we have found that:

$$\frac{T_2}{T_1} = \left(\frac{V_1}{V_2}\right)^{n-1} = \left(\frac{p_2}{p_1}\right)^{1-1/n}$$

In the case of an adiabatic process, this is written as

$$\frac{T_2}{T_1} = \left(\frac{V_1}{V_2}\right)^{\gamma-1} = \left(\frac{p_2}{p_1}\right)^{1-1/\gamma}$$

For an isothermal process $n = 1$ and the temperatures are the same.

---

### WORKED EXAMPLE 2.11

A gas is compressed adiabatically with a volume compression ratio of 10. The initial temperature is 25 °C. Calculate the final temperature, given $\gamma = 1.4$.

*Solution*

$$\frac{T_2}{T_1} = \left(\frac{V_1}{V_2}\right)^{\gamma-1} \qquad T_2 = T_1\left(\frac{V_1}{V_2}\right)^{\gamma-1} = 298(10)^{1.4-1} = \textbf{748.5 K or 475.5 °C}$$

### WORKED EXAMPLE 2.12

A gas is compressed polytropically by the law $pV^{1.2} = C$ from 1 bar and 20 °C to 12 bar. Calculate the final temperature.

*Solution*

$$\frac{T_2}{T_1} = \left(\frac{p_2}{p_1}\right)^{1-1/n} \qquad T_2 = T_1\left(\frac{p_2}{p_1}\right)^{1-1/n} = 293(12)^{1-1/1.2}$$

$$= 293(12)^{0.167} = 293(1.513) = \textbf{443.3 K}$$

### WORKED EXAMPLE 2.13

A gas is expanded from 900 kPa and 1100 °C to 100 kPa by the law $pV^{1.3} = C$. Calculate the final temperature.

*Solution*

$$\frac{T_2}{T_1} = \left(\frac{p_2}{p_1}\right)^{1-1/n} \qquad T_2 = T_1\left(\frac{p_2}{p_1}\right)^{1-1/n} = 1373\left(\frac{100}{900}\right)^{1-1/1.3}$$

$$= 1373(0.111)^{0.2308} = 1373(0.602) = \textbf{826.9 K}$$

---

1. A gas is expanded from 1 MPa and 1000 °C to 100 kPa. Calculate the final temperature when the process is
   (a) Isothermal ($n = 1$).
   (b) Polytropic ($n = 1.2$).
   (c) Adiabatic ($\gamma = 1.4$).
   (d) Polytropic ($n = 1.6$).

2. A gas is compressed from 120 kPa and 15 °C to 800 kPa. Calculate the final temperature when the process is
   (a) Isothermal ($n = 1$).
   (b) Polytropic ($n = 1.3$).
   (c) Adiabatic ($\gamma = 1.4$).
   (d) Polytropic ($n = 1.5$).

3. A gas is compressed from 200 kPa and 20 °C to 1.1 MPa by the law $pV^{1.3} = C$. The mass is 0.02 kg; $c_p = 1005$ J/kg K; $c_v = 718$ J/kg K. Calculate:
   (a) The final temperature.
   (b) The change in internal energy.
   (c) The change in enthalpy.

4. A gas is expanded from 900 kPa and 1200 °C to 120 kPa by the law $pV^{1.4} = C$. The mass is 0.015 kg; $c_p = 1100$ J/kg K; $c_v = 750$ J/kg K. Calculate:
   (a) The final temperature.
   (b) The change in internal energy.
   (c) The change in enthalpy.

## 2.4.3 *Examples involving vapour*

Problems involving vapour make use of the formula $pV^n = C$ in the same way as those involving gas. You cannot apply gas laws, however, unless the vapour is superheated into the gas region. You must make use of vapour tables so a good understanding of these is essential. This is best explained with worked examples.

### WORKED EXAMPLE 2.14

A steam turbine expands steam from 20 bar and 300 °C to 1 bar by the law $pV^{1.2} = C$. Determine for each kg flowing:

1. The initial and final volume.
2. The dryness fraction after expansion.
3. The initial and final enthalpies.
4. The change in enthalpy.

*Solution*
The system is a steady flow system in which expansion takes place as the fluid flows. The law of expansion applies in just the same way as in a closed system.

The initial volume is found from steam tables. At 20 bar and 300 °C it is super-heated, and from the tables we find $v = \mathbf{0.1255 \ m^3/kg}$.

Next apply the law $pV^{1.2} = C$:

$$p_1 V_1^{1.2} = p_2 V_2^{1.2} = 20 \times 0.1255^{1.2} = 1 \times V_2^{1.2}$$

Hence: $V_2 = \mathbf{1.523 \ m^3/kg}$

The dryness fraction is as follows:

Final volume $= 1.523 \ m^3/kg = x v_g$ at 1 bar. From the tables we find that $v_g$ is $1.694 \ m^3/kg$; hence:

$$1.523 = 1.694x \qquad \therefore \quad x = \mathbf{0.899}$$

We may now find the enthalpies in the usual way.

$h_1$ at 20 bar and 300 °C is **3025 kJ/kg**
$h_2 = h_f + x h_{fg}$ at 1 bar (wet steam)
$\quad = 417 + (0.899)(2258) = \mathbf{2447 \ kJ/kg}$

The change in enthalpy is $h_2 - h_1 = \mathbf{-578 \ kJ/kg}$.

---

## SELF-ASSESSMENT EXERCISE 2.7

1.  3 kg/s of steam is expanded in a turbine from 10 bar and 200 °C to 1.5 bar by the law $pV^{1.2} = C$. Determine:
    (a) The initial and final volumes.
    (b) The dryness fraction after expansion.
    (c) The initial and final enthalpies.
    (d) The change in enthalpy.

2.  1.5 kg/s of steam is expanded from 70 bar and 450 °C to 0.05 bar by the law $pV^{1.3} = C$. Determine:
    (a) The initial and final volumes.
    (b) The dryness fraction after expansion.
    (c) The initial and final enthalpies.
    (d) The change in enthalpy.

3.  A horizontal cylindrical vessel is divided into two sections each of 1 m³ volume, by a non-conducting piston. One section contains steam of dryness fraction 0.3 at a pressure of 1 bar, while the other contains air at the same pressure and temperature as the steam. Heat is transferred to the steam very slowly until its pressure reaches 2 bar.

    Assume that the compression of the air is adiabatic ($\gamma = 1.4$) and neglect the effect of friction between the piston and the cylinder. Calculate:
    (a) The final volume of the steam.
    (b) The mass of the steam.
    (c) The initial internal energy of the steam.
    (d) The final dryness fraction of the steam.
    (e) The final internal energy of the steam.
    (f) The heat added to the steam.

## 2.4.4 *Closed system work laws*

### Expansion of pressure with volume

We will start by studying the expansion of a fluid inside a cylinder against a piston which may do work against the surroundings.

A fluid may expand in two ways:

1.  It may expand rapidly and uncontrollably doing no useful work. In such a case the pressure could not be plotted against volume during the process. This is called an **unresisted expansion**.
2.  It may expand moving the piston. The movement is resisted by external forces so the gas pressure changes in order to overcome the external force and move the piston. In this case the movement is controlled and the variation of pressure with volume may be recorded and plotted on a *p–V* graph. Work is done against the surroundings. This process is called a **resisted expansion**.

Consider the arrangement shown in Fig. 2.15. Assume that there is no pressure outside. If the string holding the weight was cut, the gas pressure would slam the piston back and the energy would be dissipated first by acceleration of the moving parts and eventually as friction. The expansion would be unresisted.

**Fig. 2.15**  *Work transfer during a reversible expansion*

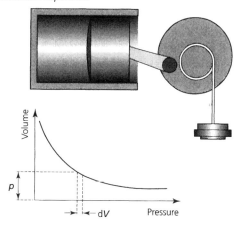

If the weights were gradually reduced, the gas would push the piston and raise the remaining weights. In this way, work would be done against the surroundings (it ends up as potential energy in the weights). The process may be repeated in many small steps, with the change in volume each time being d*V*. The pressure although changing, is *p* at any time.

This process is characterised by two important factors.

1.  The process may be reversed at any time by adding weights and the potential energy is transferred back from the surroundings as work is done on the system. The fluid may be returned to its original pressure, volume, temperature and energy.

2. The fluid force on one side of the piston is always exactly balanced by the external force (in this case due to the weights) on the other side of the piston.

The expansion or compression done in this manner is said to be **reversible** and **carried out in equilibrium**.

## Work as area under the p–V diagram

If the expansion is carried out in equilibrium, the force of the fluid must be equal to the external force $F$. It follows that $F = pA$.

When the piston moves a small distance $dx$, the work done is $dW$:

$$dW = -F\, dx = -pA\, dx = -p\, dV$$

The minus sign indicates that the work is leaving the system.

For an expansion from point 1 to point 2 it follows that the total work done is given by

$$W = -\int_{V_1}^{V_2} p\, dV$$

We must remember at this stage that our sign convention was that work leaving the system is negative.

It should be noted that some of the work is used to overcome any external pressure such as atmospheric and the useful work is reduced. Consider the system shown in Fig. 2.15 again, but this time assume that there is atmospheric pressure on the outside $p_a$. In this case It follows that

$$F + p_a A = pA \qquad \therefore \quad F = pA - p_a A$$

When the piston moves a small distance $dx$, the useful work done is $-F\, dx$:

$$-F\, dx = -(pA\, dx - p_a A\, dx) = -(p - p_a)\, dV$$

For an expansion from point 1 to point 2 it follows that the useful work done is given by

$$W = -\int_{V_1}^{V_2} (p - p_a)\, dV$$

## Work laws for closed systems

If we solve the expression $W = -\int_{V_1}^{V_2} p\, dV$ we obtain the work laws for a closed system. The solution depends upon the relationship between $p$ and $V$. The formulae now derived apply equally well to a compression process and an expansion process. Let us now solve these cases.

### Constant pressure

$$W = -\int_{V_1}^{V_2} p \, dV = -p \int_{V_1}^{V_2} dV$$

$$W = -p(V_2 - V_1)$$

### Constant volume

If $V$ is constant then $dV = 0$:

$$W = 0$$

### Hyperbolic

This is an expansion which follows the law $pV^1 = C$ and is **isothermal** when it is a gas. Substituting $p = CV^{-1}$, the expression becomes

$$W = -\int_{V_1}^{V_2} p \, dV = -C \int_{V_1}^{V_2} V^{-1} \, dV = -C \ln\left(\frac{V_2}{V_1}\right)$$

Since $pV = C$, then

$$W = -pV \ln\left(\frac{V_2}{V_1}\right)$$

and since $V_2/V_1 = p_1/p_2$ we get

$$W = -pV \ln\left(\frac{p_1}{p_2}\right)$$

In the case of a gas we can substitute $pV = mRT$, and so

$$W = -mRT \ln\left(\frac{V_2}{V_1}\right) = -mRT \ln\left(\frac{p_1}{p_2}\right)$$

### Polytropic

In this case the expansion follows the law $pV^n = C$. The solution is:

$$W = -\int_{V_1}^{V_2} p \, dV$$

but $p = CV^{-n}$, therefore

$$W = -C \int_{V_1}^{V_2} V^{-n} \, dV$$

$$= -C\left(\frac{V_2^{-n+1} - V_1^{-n+1}}{-n + 1}\right)$$

Since $C = p_1V_1$ or $p_2V_2$,

$$W = \frac{p_2V_2 - p_1V_1}{n - 1}$$

For gas only we may substitute $pV = mRT$, and so

$$W = mR\left(\frac{T_2 - T_1}{n - 1}\right)$$

### Adiabatic

Since an adiabatic case is the special case of a polytropic expansion with no heat transfer, the derivation is identical but the symbol $\gamma$ is used instead of $n$.

$$W = \frac{p_2V_2 - p_1V_1}{\gamma - 1}$$

For gas only, we may substitute $pV = mRT$ and so

$$W = mR\left(\frac{T_2 - T_1}{\gamma - 1}\right)$$

This is the special case of the polytropic process in which $Q = 0$:

$$Q = 0 \qquad W = \frac{mR\,\Delta T}{\gamma - 1}$$

Substituting for $Q$ and $\Delta U$ in the NFEE we find

$$Q + W = \Delta U$$
$$0 + \frac{mR\,\Delta T}{\gamma - 1} = mc_v\,\Delta T$$
$$\frac{R}{\gamma - 1} = c_v$$

Since $R = c_p - c_v$:

$$c_p - c_v = c_v(\gamma - 1)$$
$$\frac{c_p}{c_v} = \gamma$$

This shows that the ratio of the principal specific heat capacities is the adiabatic index. It was shown earlier that the difference is the gas constant $R$. These important relationships should be remembered.

$$c_p - c_v = R \qquad \gamma = c_p/c_v$$

## WORKED EXAMPLE 2.15

Air at a pressure of 500 kPa and volume 50 cm³ is expanded reversibly in a closed system to 800 cm³ by the law $pV^{1.3} = C$. Calculate:

1. The final pressure.
2. The work done.

### Solution

$$p_1 = 500 \text{ kPa} \qquad V_1 = 50 \times 10^{-6} \text{ m}^3 \qquad V_2 = 800 \times 10^{-6} \text{ m}^3$$

$$p_1 V_1^{1.3} = p_2 V_2^{1.3} \qquad 500 \times 10^3 (50 \times 10^{-6})^{1.3} = p_2 (800 \times 10^{-6})^{1.3}$$

$$\therefore \quad p_2 = \textbf{13.6} \times \textbf{10}^3 \textbf{ or 13.6 kPa}$$

$$W = \frac{p_2 V_2 - p_1 V_1}{n - 1} = \frac{(13.6 \times 10^3) \times (800 \times 10^{-6}) - (500 \times 10^3) \times (50 \times 10^{-6})}{1.3 - 1}$$

$$= \textbf{-47 J}$$

## WORKED EXAMPLE 2.16

Steam at 6 bar pressure and volume 100 cm³ is expanded reversibly in a closed system to 2 dm³ by the law $pV^{1.2} = C$. Calculate the work done.

### Solution

$$p_1 = 6 \text{ bar} \qquad V_1 = 100 \times 10^{-6} \text{ m}^3 \qquad V_2 = 2 \times 10^{-3} \text{ m}^3$$

$$p_2 = \frac{p_1 V_1^{1.2}}{V_2^{1.2}} = 6 \times \left( \frac{100 \times 10^{-6}}{2 \times 10^{-3}} \right)^{1.2} = 0.1648 \text{ bar}$$

$$W = \frac{p_2 V_2 - p_1 V_1}{n - 1} = \frac{(0.1648 \times 10^5) \times (2 \times 10^{-3}) - (6 \times 10^5) \times (100 \times 10^{-6})}{1.2 - 1}$$

$$= \textbf{-135.2 J}$$

## SELF-ASSESSMENT EXERCISE 2.8

1.  10 g of steam at 10 bar and 350 °C expands reversibly in a closed system to 2 bar by the law $pV^{1.3} = C$. Calculate:
    (a) The initial volume.
    (b) The final volume.
    (c) The work done.

2.  20 g of gas at 20 °C and 1 bar pressure is compressed to 9 bar by the law $pV^{1.4} = C$. Taking the gas constant $R = 287$ J/kg K calculate the work done.

(Note that for a compression process the work will turn out to be positive if you correctly identify the initial and final conditions.)

3. Gas at 600 kPa and 0.05 dm³ is expanded reversibly to 100 kPa by the law $pV^{1.35} = C$. Calculate the work done.

4. 15 g of gas is compressed isothermally from 100 kPa and 20 °C to 1 MPa pressure. The gas constant is 287 J/kg K. Calculate the work done.

5. Steam at 10 bar with a volume of 80 cm³ is expanded reversibly to 1 bar by the law $pV = C$. Calculate the work done.

6. Gas fills a cylinder fitted with a frictionless piston. The initial pressure and volume are 40 MPa and 0.05 dm³ respectively. The gas expands reversibly and polytropically to 0.5 MPa and 1 dm³ respectively. Calculate the index of expansion and the work done.

7. An air compressor commences compression when the cylinder contains 12 g at a pressure of 1.01 bar and a temperature of 20 °C. The compression is completed when the pressure is 7 bar and the temperature is 90 °C.
    The characteristic gas constant $R$ is 287 J/kg K. Assuming the process is reversible and polytropic, calculate the index of compression and the work done.

## WORKED EXAMPLE 2.17

0.2 kg of gas at 100 °C is expanded isothermally and reversibly from 1 MPa pressure to 100 kPa. Take $C_v = 718$ J/kg K and $R = 287$ J/kg K. Calculate:

1. The work transfer.
2. The change in internal energy.
3. The heat transfer.

*Solution*

$$W = -pV \ln\left(\frac{V_2}{V_1}\right) = -mRT \ln\left(\frac{V_2}{V_1}\right) = -mRT \ln\left(\frac{p_1}{p_2}\right)$$

$$= -0.2 \times 287 \times 373 \ln\left(\frac{1 \times 10^6}{1 \times 10^5}\right) = \textbf{−49 300 J or −49.3 kJ}$$

The work is leaving the system, so it is a negative work transfer.
    Since $T$ is constant:

$$\Delta U = 0 \qquad Q - 49.3 = 0 \qquad \therefore \quad Q = \textbf{49.3 kJ}$$

Note that 49.3 kJ of heat is transferred into the gas and 49.3 kJ of work is transferred out of the gas leaving the internal energy unchanged.

Repeat worked example 2.17 for an adiabatic process with $\gamma = 1.4$.

*Solution*

$$T_2 = 373 \times \left(\frac{100 \times 10^3}{1 \times 10^6}\right)^{1-1/\gamma} = 193 \text{ K}$$

$$W = -mRT(T_2 - T_1) = -0.2 \times 287 \times \frac{193 - 373}{0.4}$$

$$= -25\ 830 \text{ J}$$

For an adiabatic process, $Q = 0$:

$$Q + W = \Delta U; \quad \text{hence} \quad \Delta U = -25\ 830 \text{ J}$$

(Check: $\Delta U = mc_v \Delta T = 0.2 \times 718 \times (193 - 373) = -25\ 848$ J)

Repeat worked example 2.17 for a polytropic process with $n = 1.25$.

*Solution*

$$T_2 = 373 \times \left(\frac{100 \times 10^3}{1 \times 10^6}\right)^{1-1/n} = 235.3 \text{ K}$$

$$W = -mRT(T_2 - T_1) = -0.2 \times 287 \times \frac{235.3 - 373}{0.4}$$

$$= -31\ 605 \text{ J}$$

$$\Delta U = mc_v \Delta T = 0.2 \times 718 \times (235.3 - 373) = -19\ 773.7 \text{ J}$$

$$Q = \Delta U - W$$

$$= -19\ 773.7 - (-31\ 603) = 11\ 831.3 \text{ J}$$

Take $c_v = 718$ J/kg K and $R = 287$ J/kg K throughout.

1. 1 dm³ of gas at 100 kPa and 20 °C is compressed to 1.2 MPa reversibly by the law $pV^{1.2} = C$. Calculate:
   (a) The final volume.
   (b) The work transfer.
   (c) The final temperature.
   (d) The mass.
   (e) The change in internal energy.
   (f) The heat transfer.

2. 0.05 kg of gas at 20 bar and 1100 °C is expanded reversibly to 2 bar by the law $pV^{1.3} = C$ in a closed system. Calculate:
   (a) The initial volume.
   (b) The final volume.
   (c) The work transfer.
   (d) The change in internal energy.
   (e) The heat transfer.

3. 0.08 kg of air at 700 kPa and 800 °C is expanded adiabatically to 100 kPa in a closed system. Taking $\gamma = 1.4$ calculate:
   (a) The final temperature.
   (b) The work transfer.
   (c) The change in internal energy.

4. A horizontal cylinder is fitted with a frictionless piston and its movement is restrained by a spring, as shown in Fig. 2.16.

**Fig. 2.16** *Expansion against a spring-loaded piston*

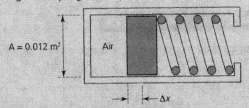

(a) The spring force is directly proportional to movement such that $\Delta F/\Delta x = k$. Show that the change in pressure is directly proportional to the change in volume such that $\Delta p/\Delta V = k/A^2$.
(b) The air is initially at a pressure and temperature of 100 kPa and 300 K respectively. Calculate the initial volume such that when the air is heated, the pressure–volume graph is a straight line that extends to the origin.
(c) The air is heated making the volume three times the original value. Calculate:
   (i) the mass
   (ii) the final pressure
   (iii) the final temperature
   (iv) the work done
   (v) the change in internal energy
   (vi) the heat transfer.

## 2.4.5 *Closed system problems involving vapour*

The solution of problems involving steam and other vapours is done in the same way as for gases, with the important proviso that gas laws must not be used. Volumes and internal energy values should be obtained from tables and property charts. This is best illustrated with a worked example.

1 kg of steam occupies a volume of 0.2 m³ at 9 bar in a closed system. The steam is heated at constant pressure until the volume is 0.3144 m³. Calculate:

1. The initial dryness fraction.
2. The final condition.
3. The work transfer.
4. The change in internal energy.
5. The heat transfer.

*Solution*

First find the initial dryness fraction:

$$V_1 = 0.2 = mx_1 v_g \text{ at 9 bar} \qquad x_1 = 0.2/(1 \times 0.2149)$$

**$x_1 = 0.931$ (initial dryness fraction).**

Now determine the specific volume after expansion is:

$$p_2 = 9 \text{ bar (constant pressure)} \qquad V_2 = 0.3144 \text{ m}^3.$$
$$V_2 = mv_2 \qquad v_2 = 0.3144/1 = 0.3144 \text{ m}^3/\text{kg}$$

First, look in the superheat tables to see if this value exists for superheat steam. We find that at 9 bar and 350 °C, the specific volume is indeed 0.3144 m³/kg.

**The final condition is superheated to 350 °C.**

Note that if $v_2$ was less than $v_g$ at 9 bar the steam would be wet and $x_2$ would have to be found.

Next find the work:

$$W = -p(V_2 - V_1) = -9 \times 10^5(0.3144 - 0.2) = -102\,950 \text{ J}$$

**$W = -102.95$ kJ (energy leaving the system)**

Next determine the internal energy from steam tables:

$$U_1 = mu_1 \quad \text{and} \quad u_1 = u_f + x_1 u_{fg} \text{ at 9 bar}$$
$$u_{fg} \text{ at 9 bar} = u_g - u_f = 2581 - 742 = 1839 \text{ kJ/kg}$$
$$U_1 = 1[742 + 0.931(1839)] = 2454 \text{ kJ}$$
$$U_2 = mu_2 \quad \text{and} \quad u_2 = u \text{ at 9 bar and 350 °C} = 2877 \text{ kJ/kg}$$
$$U_2 = mu_2 = 1(2877) = 2877 \text{ kJ}.$$

**The change in internal energy $= U_2 - U_1 = 423$ kJ (increased)**

Finally deduce the heat transfer from the NFEE:

$$Q + W = \Delta U$$

hence:  $Q = \Delta U - W = 423 - (-102.95)$

**$Q = 526$ kJ (energy entering the system)**

1. 0.2 kg of dry saturated steam at 10 bar pressure is expanded reversibly in a closed system to 1 bar by the law $pV^{1.2} = C$. Calculate:
   (a) The initial volume.
   (b) The final volume.
   (c) The work transfer.
   (d) The dryness fraction.
   (e) The change in internal energy.
   (f) The heat transfer.

2. Steam at 15 bar and 250 °C is expanded reversibly in a closed system to 5 bar. At this pressure the steam is just dry saturated. For a mass of 1 kg calculate:
   (a) The final volume.
   (b) The change in internal energy.
   (c) The work done.
   (d) The heat transfer.

3. Repeat question 2 but with an initial pressure of 30 bar.

# 3 Internal combustion engines and gas turbine engines

When you have completed this chapter, you should have a basic understanding of the following topics and be able to solve problems concerning them:

- The second law of thermodynamics.
- Entropy.
- Theoretical engine cycles.
- How real engines are tested for performance.
- How the performance of real engines may be improved.

## 3.1 The second law of thermodynamics

The second law of thermodynamics is not something that can be written as a simple statement or formulae. It is a set of observations concerning the way that things flow or run as time progresses forward. It encompasses many observations such as 'water normally flows from high levels to low levels' and 'heat normally flows from hot to cold'. In this module, you must concern yourself only with how the second law relates to heat engines and the efficiency of a heat engine.

In the context of heat engines, the second law may be summed as:

*'No heat engine can be 100% efficient'*

This should become apparent in the following sections.

### 3.1.1 *Heat engines*

Nearly all motive power is derived from heat using some form of heat engine, for example:

- Steam power plant.
- Gas turbines.
- Jet engines.
- Internal combustion engines.

**Fig. 3.1** *Electric, hydraulic and heat motors*

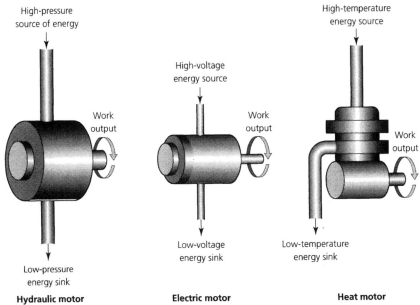

A heat engine requires a source of hot energy. We get this by burning fossil fuel or by nuclear fission. The main sources of natural heat are solar and geothermal. In order to understand the basic theory, it might help to draw an analogy with a hydraulic motor and an electric motor. All motors require a high level source of energy and must exhaust at a low level of energy.

## Hydraulic motor

Fluid power is transported by the flow $Q$ m$^3$/s. The energy contained in a volume $Q$ m$^3$ of liquid at a pressure $p$ is the flow energy given by the expression $pQ$. The hydraulic motor requires a source of liquid at a high pressure $p_1$ and exhausts at a lower pressure $p_2$. The energy supplied is $p_1 Q$ and some of this is converted into work. The energy in the low-pressure liquid is $p_2 Q$. For a perfect motor with no losses due to friction, the law of energy conservation gives the work output and efficiency ($\eta$) as follows:

$$W_{out} = p_1 Q - p_2 Q = Q(p_1 - p_2)$$

$$\eta = \frac{W_{out}}{\text{energy input}} = \frac{W_{out}}{p_1 Q} = \frac{Q(p_1 - p_2)}{p_1 Q} = \frac{p_1 - p_2}{p_1} = 1 - \frac{p_2}{p_1}$$

## Electric motor

Electric power is transported by the current. Electrical energy is the product of the charge $Q$ coulombs and the electric potential $V$ volts. The energy input at a high voltage is $V_1 Q$ and the energy exhausted at low voltage is $V_2 Q$. For a perfect motor with no losses due to friction, the work output and efficiency are found from the law of energy conservation as follows:

$$W_{out} = V_1 Q - V_2 Q = Q(V_1 - V_2)$$
$$\eta = \frac{W_{out}}{\text{energy input}} = \frac{W_{out}}{V_1 Q} = \frac{Q(V_1 - V_2)}{V_1 Q} = \frac{V_1 - V_2}{V_1} = 1 - \frac{V_2}{V_1}$$

### Heat motor

Temperature is by analogy the equivalent of pressure and electric potential. In order to complete the analogy, we need something that is equivalent to volume and electric charge that transports the energy. It is not difficult to visualise a volume of liquid flowing through a hydraulic motor. Nor is it impossible to visualise a flow of electrons bearing electric charge through an electric motor. However, it is impossible to visualise something flowing through our ideal heat engine that transports pure heat, but the analogy tells us there must be something so let us suppose there is a new property called **entropy** and give it a symbol $S$. Entropy must have units of energy per degree of temperature or joules per kelvin (J/K), and is dealt with more fully later on.

The energy supplied at temperature $T_1$ is $T_1 S$ and the energy exhausted is $T_2 S$. For a perfect motor with no losses due to friction, the law of energy conservation gives the work output and efficiency as:

$$W_{out} = T_1 S - T_2 S = S(T_1 - T_2)$$
$$\eta = \frac{W_{out}}{\text{energy input}} = \frac{W_{out}}{T_1 S} = \frac{S(T_1 - T_2)}{T_1 S} = \frac{T_1 - T_2}{T_1} = 1 - \frac{T_2}{T_1}$$

## 3.1.2 *Efficiency*

In our perfect motors, the energy conversion process is 100% efficient but we may not have converted all the energy supplied into work and energy may be wasted in the exhaust. In the case of the electric motor, the lowest value for $V_2$ (as far as we know) is ground voltage zero, so theoretically we can obtain 100% efficiency by exhausting the electric charge with no residual energy.

In the case of the hydraulic motor, the lowest pressure we can exhaust to is atmospheric so we always waste some energy in the exhausted liquid.

In the case of the heat motor, the lowest temperature to which we can exhaust is ambient conditions, typically 300 K, so there is a lot of residual energy in the exhaust. Only by exhausting to absolute zero can we extract all the energy.

A model heat engine is usually represented by Fig. 3.2. (Note that the word engine is often preferred to motor.)

**Fig. 3.2** *Model of an ideal heat engine*

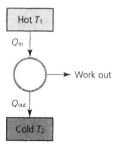

- The energy transfer from the hot source is $Q_{in}$ joules.
- The energy transfer rate from the hot source is $\Phi_{in}$ watts.

- The energy transfer to the cold sink is $Q_{out}$ joules.
- The energy transfer rate to the cold sink is $\Phi_{out}$ watts.

- The work output is $W$ joules.
- The power output is $P$ watts.

By considering the total conservation of energy, it follows that the energy converted into work must be

$$W = Q_{in} - Q_{out} \text{ joules} \quad \text{or}$$
$$P = \Phi_{in} - \Phi_{out} \text{ watts}$$

The efficiency of any machine is the ratio output/input, so the thermal efficiency of a heat engine may be developed as follows:

$$\eta_{th} = \frac{W}{Q_{in}} \qquad W = Q_{in} - Q_{out}$$
$$\eta_{th} = \frac{Q_{in} - Q_{out}}{Q_{in}} = 1 - \frac{Q_{out}}{Q_{in}}$$

In terms of energy transfer rates in watts this is written as

$$\eta_{th} = 1 - \frac{\Phi_{out}}{\Phi_{in}}$$

It follows from our analogy that $Q_{in} = ST_1$ and $Q_{out} = ST_2$ and confirms $\eta = 1 - (T_2/T_1)$.

---

### SELF-ASSESSMENT EXERCISE 3.1

1. A heat engine is supplied with 60 MW of energy and produces 20 MW of power. What is the thermal efficiency and the heat lost?

2. A heat engine is supplied with 40 kJ of energy that it converts into work with 25% efficiency. What is the work output and the heat lost?

## 3.1.3 *Practical heat engine considerations*

Let us consider how we might design a practical heat engine with a piston, connecting rod and crankshaft mechanism. Figure 3.3 shows how heat may be passed to a gas inside a cylinder causing it to expand. This pushes a piston and makes it do some work. This at first looks like a good way of converting heat into work but the problem is that it works only once and cannot convert heat into work continuously.

No practical heat engine has ever been invented that continuously converts heat directly into work as supposed in our ideal model. Practical heat engines use a working fluid such as gas or steam. A cycle of thermodynamic processes is conducted on the fluid with the end result being a conversion of heat into work.

---

**Fig. 3.3** *Obtaining work with a piston*

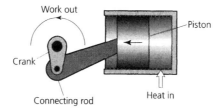

First energy is given to the working fluid by use of a heat transfer at a hot temperature. Next we must convert as much of this energy as possible into work by allowing the fluid to expand. Our studies of polytropic expansions tell us that the pressure, volume and temperature all change as the gas or vapour gives up its energy as work. The pressure is vitally important to produce a motivating force on the piston.

Having extracted as much energy as possible from the working fluid, we must return it back to the starting condition in order to repeat the process. To do this, we must raise the pressure of the fluid back to the high level with some form of compression.

A simple reversal of the expansion process would return the fluid back to the original pressure and temperature. However, this would require us to give back all the work we got out so nothing is gained.

The only way we can return the fluid back to a high pressure with less work involves cooling it first. In fact, if it is to be a heat engine, we must have a cooling process as indicated in our model.

We have deduced that a practical heat engine must meet the following criteria:

• It must produce work continuously.
• It must return the working fluid back to the same pressure and temperature at the beginning of every cycle.

A model of a practical engine is shown in Fig. 3.4. This indicates that we need four processes: heating, expansion, cooling and compression. This may be achieved practically

**Fig. 3.4** *Practical model for a heat engine*

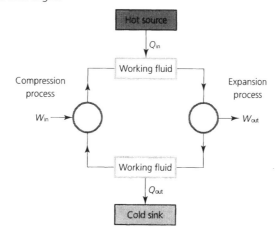

using either closed system processes (as in a mechanism with a piston, connecting rod and crankshaft) or open system processes (such as with a steam boiler, turbine, cooler and pump).

### 3.1.4 *Entropy and heat engines*

**Temperature–entropy diagrams**

We have just discovered that entropy is a property that conveys energy at a temperature such that, in our ideal heat engine, the energy is given by the expression $Q = ST$. Entropy is a property that is closely associated with the second law of thermodynamics.

In thermodynamics there are two forms of energy transfer: work ($W$) and heat ($Q$). You should already be familiar with the theory of work laws in closed systems and know that the area under a pressure–volume diagram gives work transfer. By analogy there should be a property that can be plotted against temperature such that the area under the graph gives the heat transfer. This property is **entropy** and it is given the symbol $S$. This idea implies that entropy is a property that can be transported by a fluid. Consider a $p$–$V$ and $T$–$s$ graph for a reversible expansion (Fig. 3.5).

**Fig. 3.5** *Representing an expansion on a p–v and a T–s diagram*

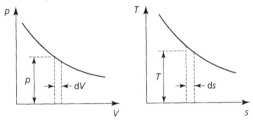

From the $p$–$V$ graph we have $W = \int p\, \mathrm{d}V$

From the $T$–$s$ graph we have $Q = \int T\, \mathrm{d}s$

This is the way entropy was developed for thermodynamics, and from the above we get the following definition:

**$\mathrm{d}S = \mathrm{d}Q/T$**

The units of entropy are hence J/K. Specific entropy has a symbol $s$ and the units are J/kg K.

It should be pointed out that there are other definitions of entropy but this one is the most meaningful for thermodynamics. A suitable integration will enable you to solve the entropy change for a fluid process. Those wishing to do studies in greater depth are referred to Appendices A and B.

Entropy values for steam may be found in your thermodynamic tables in the columns headed $s_f$, $s_{fg}$ and $s_g$.

- $s_f$ is the specific entropy of saturated liquid.
- $s_{fg}$ is the change in specific entropy during the latent stage.
- $s_g$ is the specific entropy of dry saturated vapour.

### Temperature–entropy (T–s) diagram for vapours

If you plot the specific entropy for saturated liquid ($s_f$) and for dry saturated vapour ($s_g$) against temperature, you would obtain the saturation curve. Lines of constant dryness fraction and constant pressure may be shown (Fig. 3.6).

**Fig. 3.6** *T–s diagram for steam/water*

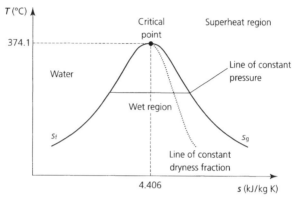

### Specific enthalpy–specific entropy (h–s) diagram

This diagram is especially useful for steady flow processes (Fig. 3.7). The diagram is obtained by plotting $h_g$ against $s_g$ and $h_f$ against $s_f$ to obtain the characteristic saturation curve. The two curves meet at the critical point C. Lines of constant pressure, temperature and dryness are superimposed on the diagram. This is an extremely useful chart and is available commercially. If any two coordinates are known, a point can be obtained on the chart and all other relevant values may be read off. *h–s* charts are especially useful for solving isentropic processes because the process shows as a vertical line on this graph.

### Isentropic processes

The word **isentropic** means constant entropy and is a very important thermodynamic process. It occurs in particular when a process is reversible and adiabatic. This means that there is no heat transfer to or from the fluid and no internal heat generation due to friction. In such a process it follows that if $dQ$ is zero then $dS$ must be zero. Since there is no area under the *T–s* graph, the graph must be a vertical line.

There is another case where the entropy is constant. For example, if there is friction in the process generating heat but this is lost through cooling, then the net result is zero heat transfer and constant entropy. However, you do not need to be concerned with this at this stage.

**Fig. 3.7** *Enthalpy–entropy chart for steam*

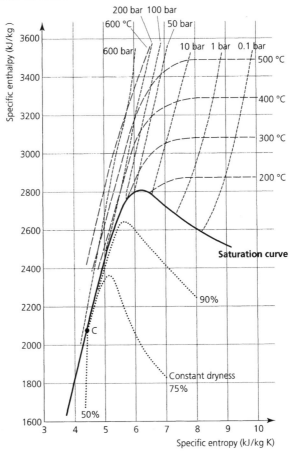

**WORKED EXAMPLE 3.1**

Steam at 2 bar and 150 °C is expanded reversibly and adiabatically to 1 bar. Calculate the final dryness fraction and the enthalpy change.

***Solution***
$h_1$ at 2 bar and 150 °C = 2770 kJ/kg
$s_1$ at 2 bar and 150 °C is 7.280 kJ/kg K.
Because the process is adiabatic and reversible, the entropy remains the same.
$s_2$ at 1 bar and assumed wet is $s_f + xs_{fg} = s_1$

$$7.280 = 1.303 + x(6.056)$$
$$x = 0.987$$

$h_2$ at 1 bar and 0.987 dry = $h_f + xh_{fg}$
$h_2 = 417 + 0.987(2258) = 2645.6$ kJ/kg

Hence: $\Delta h = 2645.6 - 2770 = -124.4$ kJ/kg

A steam turbine expands 60 kg/s from 40 bar and 300 °C to 4 bar reversibly and adiabatically (isentropic). Calculate the theoretical power output.

*Solution*

$\Phi + P = \Delta E$ per second (SFEE)

The process is adiabatic, $\Phi = 0$, and the only energy term to use is enthalpy.

$P = \Delta H$ per second.

$h_1$ at 40 bar and 300 °C = 2963 kJ/kg

$s_1$ at 40 bar and 300 °C is 6.364 kJ/kg K.

$s_2$ at 4 bar and assumed wet is $s_f + x s_{fg} = s_1$

$$6.364 = 1.776 + x(5.121)$$
$$\therefore \quad x = 0.896$$

$h_2$ at 4 bar and 0.896 dry $= h_f + x h_{fg}$

$h_2 = 605 + 0.896(2134) = 2517$ kJ/kg

$$P = \Delta H \text{ per second} = 60(2517 - 2963) = -26756 \text{ kW (out of system)}$$

1. A turbine expands 40 kg/s of steam from 20 bar and 250 °C reversibly and adiabatically to 0.5 bar. Calculate the theoretical power output.

2. A turbine expands 4 kg/s of steam from 50 bar and 300 °C reversibly and adiabatically to 0.1 bar. Calculate the theoretical power output.

3. A turbine expands 20 kg/s of steam from 800 bar and 400 °C reversibly and adiabatically to 0.2 bar. Calculate the theoretical power output.

4. A turbine expands 1 kg/s of steam reversibly and adiabatically. The inlet conditions are 10 bar and dry saturated. The outlet pressure is 3 bar. Calculate the theoretical power output.

# 3.2 Theoretical cycles for engines

When you have completed this section you should be able to explain and solve problems involving the following:

- The Carnot principle.
- The theoretical cycle of a spark ignition engine.
- The theoretical cycles for compression ignition engines.
- The theoretical cycle for a gas turbine engine.

Internal combustion engines fall into two groups: those that use a sparking plug to ignite the fuel (spark ignition engines) and those that use the natural temperature of the compressed air to ignite the fuel (compression ignition engines).

Engines can also be grouped into those that use non-flow processes and those that use flow processes. For example, non-flow processes are used in piston engines; flow processes are used in gas turbine engines.

Theoretical cycles are made up of ideal thermodynamic processes to resemble as closely as possible those that occur in a real engine. Many of these cycles are based on air as the working fluid and are called **air standard cycles**. Before looking at air standard cycles, we should consider the most efficient cycle possible, and this is the Carnot cycle.

### 3.2.1 *The Carnot principle*

A man called Sadi Carnot deduced that if the heat transfers from the hot reservoir and to the cold sump were done at constant temperature (isothermal processes), then the efficiency of the engine would be the maximum possible.

The reasoning behind this is as follows (refer to Fig. 3.8).

Consider heat being transferred from a hot body A to a slightly cooler body B. The temperature of body A falls and the temperature of body B rises until both bodies are at the same temperature.

If body B is now raised in temperature by heat transfer from the surroundings, it becomes the hotter body and the heat flow is reversed from B to A. If body A returns to its original temperature then the nett heat transfers between A and B is zero. However, body B is now hotter than its original temperature so there has been a nett heat transfer from the surroundings. The heat transfer process is hence not reversible as external help was needed to reverse the process.

If it were possible to transfer heat with no temperature difference from A to B then it could be reversed with no external help. Such a process is an **isothermal** process. Isothermal heat transfer is possible – for example, evaporation of water in a boiler is isothermal.

**Fig. 3.8** *Illustration of irreversible heat transfer*

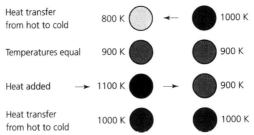

### Closed system Carnot cycle

The cycle could be conducted on gas or vapour in a closed or open cycle. The cycle described here is for gas in a cylinder fitted with a piston. It consists of four closed system processes as follows:

1 to 2    The fluid is compressed isentropically. Work is put in and no heat transfer occurs (Fig. 3.9).

**Fig. 3.9**    *First stroke in a Carnot cycle*

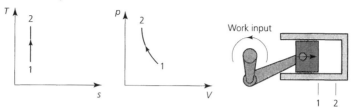

2 to 3    The fluid is heated isothermally. This could only occur if it is heated as it expands, so work is taken out and heat is put in (Fig. 3.10).

**Fig. 3.10**    *Second stroke in a Carnot cycle*

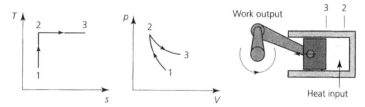

3 to 4    The fluid continues to expand isentropically with no heat transfer. Work output is obtained (Fig. 3.11).

**Fig. 3.11**    *Third stroke in a Carnot cycle*

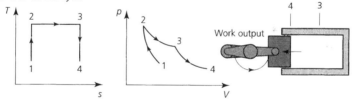

4 to 1    The fluid is cooled isothermally. This can only occur if it cools as it is compressed, so work is put in and heat is taken out. At the end of this process every thing is returned to the initial condition (Fig. 3.12).

**Fig. 3.12**    *Fourth stroke in a Carnot cycle*

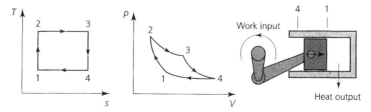

The total work taken out is $W_{out}$ and the total work put in is $W_{in}$.

To be an engine, $W_{out}$ must be larger than $W_{in}$ and a nett amount of work is obtained from the cycle. It also follows that since the area under a $p$–$V$ graph represents the work done, then the area enclosed by the $p$–$V$ diagram represents the nett work transfer.

It also follows that since the area under the $T$–$s$ graph represents the heat transfer, then the area enclosed on the $T$–$s$ diagram represents the nett heat transfer (Fig. 3.13). This is true for all cycles and also for real engines.

**Fig. 3.13** *The complete p–v and T–s diagrams for the Carnot cycle*

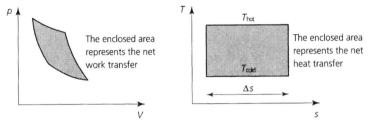

Applying the first law, it follows that

$$Q_{net} = W_{net}$$

For isothermal heat transfers, $Q = \int T \, ds = T \, \Delta S$ since $T$ is constant. The efficiency would then be given by

$$\eta_{th} = 1 - \frac{Q_{out}}{Q_{in}} = 1 - \frac{T_{cold} \, \Delta s_{cold}}{T_{hot} \, \Delta s_{hot}}$$

It is apparent from the $T$–$s$ diagram that the change in entropy $\Delta s$ is the same at the hot and cold temperatures. It follows that

$$\eta_{th} = 1 - \frac{T_{cold}}{T_{hot}}$$

This expression, which is the same as that used for the ideal model, gives the **Carnot efficiency** and it is used as a target figure that cannot be surpassed (in fact not even attained).

---

### WORKED EXAMPLE 3.3

A heat engine draws heat from a combustion chamber at 300 °C and exhausts to atmosphere at 10 °C. What is the maximum possible thermal efficiency that could be achieved?

*Solution*
The maximum efficiency possible is the Carnot efficiency. Remember to use absolute temperatures:

$$\eta_{th} = 1 - \frac{T_{cold}}{T_{hot}} = 1 - \frac{273 + 10}{273 + 300} = 1 - \frac{283}{573} = 0.505 \text{ or } \mathbf{50.5\%}$$

---

## 3.2.2 *Spark ignition engine*

### The Otto cycle

The ideal cycle is named after Count N.A. Otto. It represents the ideal cycle for a spark ignition engine. In an ideal spark ignition engine, there are four processes (Fig. 3.14).

**Fig. 3.14** *The four processes of a spark ignition cycle*

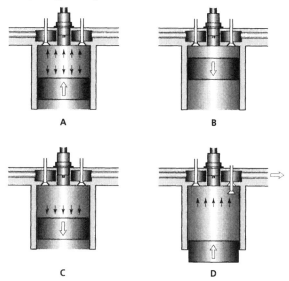

1. **Compression stroke**   Air and fuel are mixed and compressed so rapidly that there is no time for heat to be lost (diagram A). In other words, the compression is adiabatic. Work must be done to compress the gas.

2. **Ignition**   Just before the point of maximum compression, the air is hot and a spark ignites the mixture causing an explosion (diagram B). This produces a rapid rise in the pressure and temperature. The process is idealised as a constant volume process in the Otto cycle.

3. **Expansion or working stroke**   The explosion is followed by an adiabatic expansion pushing the piston and giving out work (diagram C).

4. **Exhaust**   At the end of the working stroke, there is still some pressure in the cylinder. This is released suddenly by the opening of an exhaust valve (diagram D). This is idealised by a constant volume drop in pressure in the Otto cycle. In four-stroke

engines a second cycle is performed to push out the products of combustion and draw in fresh air and fuel. It is only the power cycle that we are concerned with.

The four ideal processes that make up the Otto cycle are as follows:

1 to 2   The air is compressed reversibly and adiabatically. Work is put in and no heat transfer occurs (Fig. 3.15).

**Fig. 3.15**   *The compression stroke of an Otto cycle*

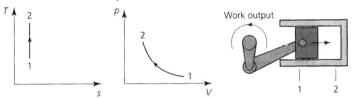

2 to 3   The air is heated at constant volume. No work is done (Fig. 3.16): $Q_{in} = mc_v(T_3 - T_2)$.

**Fig. 3.16**   *Constant volume heating in an Otto cycle*

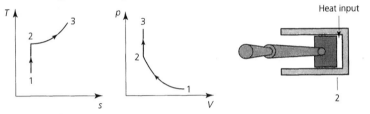

3 to 4   The air expands reversibly and adiabatically with no heat transfer back to its original volume. Work output is obtained (Fig. 3.17).

**Fig. 3.17**   *The expansion stroke of an Otto cycle*

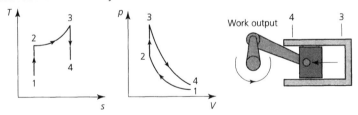

4 to 1   The air is cooled at constant volume back to its original pressure and temperature. No work is done (Fig. 3.18): $Q_{out} = mc_v(T_4 - T_1)$.

**Fig. 3.18**   *The constant volume cooling in an Otto cycle*

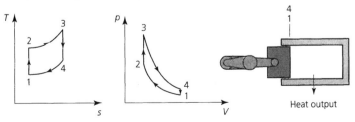

The total heat transfer into the system during one cycle is $Q_{net} = Q_{in} - Q_{out}$

The total work output per cycle is $W_{net}$

From the first law of thermodynamics, $Q_{net} = W_{net}$

### Efficiency

$$\eta = \frac{W_{net}}{Q_{in}} = 1 - \frac{Q_{out}}{Q_{in}} = 1 - \frac{mc_v(T_4 - T_1)}{mc_v(T_3 - T_2)} = 1 - \left(\frac{T_4 - T_1}{T_3 - T_2}\right)$$

For the process 1 to 2 we may use the rule

$$\frac{T_2}{T_1} = \left(\frac{V_1}{V_2}\right)^{\gamma-1} = r_v^{\gamma-1}$$

For the process 3 to 4 we may similarly write

$$\frac{T_3}{T_4} = \left(\frac{V_4}{V_3}\right)^{\gamma-1} = r_v^{\gamma-1}$$

where $r_v$ is the volume compression ratio ($= V_1/V_2 = V_4/V_3$). It follows that

$$\frac{T_2}{T_1} = \frac{T_3}{T_4}; \qquad \frac{T_4}{T_1} = \frac{T_3}{T_2}$$

and

$$\eta = 1 - \left(\frac{T_4 - T_1}{T_3 - T_2}\right) = 1 - \frac{(T_3 T_1/T_2) - T_1}{(T_2 T_4/T_1) - T_2} = 1 - \frac{T_1[(T_3/T_2) - 1]}{T_2[(T_4/T_1) - 1]}$$

$$\frac{T_4}{T_1} = \frac{T_3}{T_2} \quad \text{then} \quad \frac{T_4}{T_1} - 1 = \frac{T_3}{T_2} - 1$$

$$\eta = 1 - \frac{T_1}{T_2} = 1 - \frac{T_4}{T_3} = 1 - \frac{1}{r_v^{\gamma-1}} = 1 - r_v^{1-\gamma}$$

Since this theoretical cycle is carried out on air for which $\gamma = 1.4$, the efficiency of an Otto cycle is given by $\eta = 1 - r_v^{0.4}$.

This shows that the thermal efficiency depends only on the compression ratio. If the compression ratio is increased, the efficiency is improved. This in turn increases the temperature ratios between the two isentropic processes and explains why the efficiency is improved.

### WORKED EXAMPLE 3.4

An Otto cycle is conducted as follows. Air at 100 kPa and 20 °C is compressed reversibly and adiabatically. The air is then heated at constant volume to 1500 °C. The air then expands reversibly and adiabatically back to the original volume and is cooled at constant volume back to the original pressure and temperature. The volume compression ratio is 8. Calculate:

1. The thermal efficiency.
2. The heat input per kg of air.
3. The net work output per kg of air.
4. The maximum cycle pressure.

$c_v = 718$ kJ/kg     $\gamma = 1.4$     $R = 287$ J/kg K

*Solution*

Remember to use absolute temperatures throughout and solve for a mass of 1 kg.

$T_1 = 20 + 273 = 293$ K       $T_3 = 1500 + 273 = 1773$ K       $r_v = 8$

$\eta = 1 - r^{1-\gamma} = 1 - 8^{-0.4} = 0.565$ or **56.5%**

$T_2 = T_1(V_1/V_2)^{\gamma-1} = 293(8^{0.4}) = 673.1$ K
$Q_{in} = mc_v(T_3 - T_2) = 1 \times 718(1773 - 673.1) = 789\,700$ J/kg $= 789.7$ kJ/kg
$W_{net} = \eta Q_{in} = 0.56 \times 789.7 = $ **446.2 kJ/kg**

From the gas law we have

$$p_3 = \frac{p_1 V_1 T_3}{T_1 V_3} = \frac{100\,000 \times V_1 \times 1773}{293 \times V_3}$$

$V_1/V_3 = 8$

$$p_3 = \frac{100\,000 \times 1773}{293} \times 8 = \textbf{4.84 MPa}$$

If you have followed the principles used here you should be able to solve any cycle.

### SELF-ASSESSMENT EXERCISE 3.4

Take $c_v = 0.718$ kJ/kg K, $R = 287$ J/kg K and $\gamma = 1.4$ throughout.

1. An Otto cycle has a volume compression ratio of 9/1. The heat input is 500 kJ/kg. At the start of compression the pressure and temperature are 100 kPa and 40 °C respectively. Calculate:
   (a) The thermal efficiency.
   (b) The maximum cycle temperature.
   (c) The maximum pressure.
   (d) The net work output per kg of air.

2. (a) Calculate the volume compression ratio required of an Otto cycle which will produce an efficiency of 60%.
   (b) The pressure and temperature before compression are 105 kPa and 25 °C respectively. The net work output is 500 kJ/kg. Calculate:
   (i)   The heat input
   (ii)  The maximum temperature
   (iii) The maximum pressure.

3. An Otto cycle uses a volume compression ratio of 9.5/1. The pressure and temperature before compression are 100 kPa and 40 °C respectively. The mass of air used is 11.5 g/cycle. The heat input is 600 kJ/kg. The cycle is performed 3000 times per minute. Determine:
   (a) The thermal efficiency.
   (b) The net work output.
   (c) The net power output.

4. An Otto cycle with a volume compression ratio of 9 is required to produce a nett work output of 450 kJ/cycle. Calculate the mass of air to be used if the maximum and minimum temperatures in the cycle are 1300 °C and 20 °C respectively.

5. The working of a petrol engine can be approximated to an Otto cycle with a compression ratio of 8 using air at 1 bar and 288 K with heat addition of 2 MJ/kg. Calculate the heat rejected and the work done per kg of air.

Now let's move on to study engines with compression ignition.

### 3.2.3 *Compression ignition engines*

The invention of compression ignition engines, commonly known as diesel engines, was credited to Rudolf Diesel, although many other people worked on similar engines. The basic principle is that when high compression ratios are used, the air becomes hot enough to make the fuel detonate without a spark. Diesel's first engine used coal dust blasted into the combustion chamber with compressed air. This developed into blasting in oil with compressed air. In modern engines the fuel oil is injected directly into the cylinder as fine droplets. There are two ideal cycles for these engines: the dual combustion cycle and the diesel cycle.

#### Dual combustion cycle

This is the air standard cycle for a modern fast-running diesel engine. First the air is compressed isentropically making it hot. Fuel injection starts before the point of maximum compression. After a short delay in which fuel accumulates in the cylinder, the fuel warms up to the air temperature and detonates, causing a sudden rise in pressure. This is ideally a constant volume heating process. Further injection keeps the fuel burning as the volume increases and produces a constant pressure heating process. After cut off, the hot air expands isentropically, and at the end of the stroke the exhaust valve opens producing a sudden drop in pressure. This is ideally a constant volume cooling process. The ideal cycle is shown in Fig. 3.19.

The processes are as follows:

1–2  Reversible adiabatic (isentropic) compression.
2–3  Constant volume heating.
3–4  Constant pressure heating.
4–5  Reversible adiabatic (isentropic) expansion.
5–1  Constant volume cooling.

**Fig. 3.19** *The dual combustion cycle*

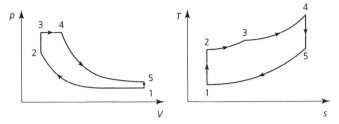

The analysis of the cycle is as follows:

The heat is supplied in two stages, hence: $Q_{in} = mc_p(T_4 - T_3) + mc_v(T_3 - T_2)$
The heat rejected is: $Q_{out} = mc_v(T_5 - T_1)$

The thermal efficiency may be found as follows.

$$\eta = 1 - \frac{Q_{out}}{Q_{in}} = 1 - \frac{mc_v(T_5 - T_1)}{mc_v(T_3 - T_2) + mc_p(T_4 - T_3)} = 1 - \frac{T_5 - T_1}{(T_3 - T_2) + \gamma(T_4 - T_3)}$$

The formula can be further developed to show that

$$\eta = 1 - \frac{k\beta^\gamma - 1}{[(k - 1) + \gamma k(\beta - 1)]r_v^{\gamma-1}}$$

where $r_v$ is the **volume compression ratio** ($r_v = V_1/V_2$); $\beta$ is the **cut off ratio** ($\beta = V_4/V_3$); and $k$ is the ratio $p_3/p_2$.

Most students will find this adequate to solve problems concerning the dual combustion cycle. Generally, the method of solution involves finding all the temperatures by application of the gas laws.

Those requiring a detailed analysis of the cycle should study the following derivation:

$$\eta = 1 - \frac{Q_{out}}{Q_{in}} = 1 - \frac{T_5 - T_1}{(T_3 - T_2) + \gamma(T_4 - T_3)}$$

Obtain all the temperatures in terms of $T_2$.

*Isentropic compression*: 1 to 2

$$T_1 = T_2\left(\frac{V_2}{V_1}\right)^{\gamma-1} = \frac{T_2}{r_v^{\gamma-1}}$$

*Constant volume heating*: 2 to 3, note $V_3 = V_2$

$$T_3 = \frac{p_3 V_3 T_2}{p_2 V_2} = \frac{p_3 T_2}{p_2} = kT_2$$

*Constant pressure heating*: 3 to 4, note $p_3 = p_4$

$$T_4 = \frac{p_4 V_4 T_3}{p_3 V_3} = \frac{V_4 T_3}{V_3} = \beta T_3 = \beta kT_2$$

*Isentropic expansion*: 4 to 5

$$T_5 = T_4 \left(\frac{V_4}{V_5}\right)^{\gamma-1} = T_4 \left(\frac{V_4 V_2}{V_5 V_2}\right)^{\gamma-1} = T_4 \left(\frac{\beta}{r_v}\right)^{\gamma-1} = \frac{k\beta^\gamma T_2}{r_r^{\gamma-1}}$$

Substitute for all temperatures in the efficiency formula.

$$\eta = 1 - \frac{(k\beta^\gamma T_2/r_r^{\gamma-1}) - (T_2/r_v^{\gamma-1})}{(kT_2 - T_2) + \gamma(\beta kT_2 - kT_2)} = 1 - \frac{(k\beta^\gamma/r_r^{\gamma-1}) - (1/r_v^{\gamma-1})}{(k-1) + \gamma(\beta k - k)}$$

$$= 1 - \frac{k\beta^\gamma - 1}{[(k-1) + \gamma k(\beta - 1)]r_v^{\gamma-1}}$$

Note that if $\beta = 1$, the cycle becomes an Otto cycle and the efficiency formulae becomes the same as for an Otto cycle.

---

## WORKED EXAMPLE 3.5

In a dual combustion cycle, the compression starts from 1 bar and 20 °C. The compression ratio is 18/1 and the cut off ratio is 1.15. The maximum cycle pressure is 1360 K. The total heat input is 1 kJ per cycle. Calculate:

1. The thermal efficiency of the cycle.
2. The net work output per cycle.
3. Check that the efficiency does not contravene the Carnot principle.

### Solution
Known data:

$T_1 = 20 + 273 = 293$ K (the hottest temperature is $T_4 = 1360$ K)

$\beta = 1.15$ $\quad r_v = 18$ $\quad \gamma = 1.4$

$T_2 = T_1 r_v^{\gamma-1} = 293 \times 18^{0.4} = 931$ K

$T_3 = \frac{V_3 T_4}{V_4} = \frac{T_4}{\beta} = \frac{1360}{1.15} = 1183$ K

$\frac{p_3}{p_2} = k = \frac{T_3}{T_2} = 1.27$

$\eta = 1 - \dfrac{k\beta^\gamma - 1}{[(k-1) + \gamma k(\beta - 1)]r_v^{\gamma-1}}$

$= 1 - \dfrac{1.27 \times 1.15^{1.4} - 1}{\{(1.27 - 1) + [1.4 \times 1.27 \times (1.15 - 1)]\} \times 18^{0.4}}$

$= \mathbf{0.68 \text{ or } 68\%}$

$W_{net} = \eta \times Q_{in} = 0.68 \times 1 = \mathbf{0.68 \text{ kJ per cycle}}$

The Carnot efficiency should be higher.

$\eta = 1 - \dfrac{T_{cold}}{T_{hot}} = 1 - \dfrac{293}{1360} = \mathbf{0.785}$

The figure of 0.68 is lower so the Carnot principle has not been contravened.

A dual combustion cycle has a compression ratio of 18/1. The maximum pressure in the cycle is 9 MPa and the maximum temperature is 2000 °C. The pressure and temperature before compression are 115 kPa and 25 °C respectively. Calculate:

1. The cut off ratio.
2. The cycle efficiency.
3. The net work output per kg of air.

Assume $\gamma = 1.4$     $c_p = 1.005$ kJ/kg K     $c_v = 0.718$ kJ/kg K.

*Solution*
Known data:

$$T_1 = 298 \text{ K} \quad T_4 = 2273 \text{ K} \quad p_3 = p_4 = 9 \text{ MPa} \quad p_1 = 115 \text{ kPa}$$
$$V_1/V_2 = V_1/V_3 = 18 \qquad V_2 = V_3$$

$$T_2 = 298 \times 18^{\gamma-1} = 947 \text{ K}$$

$$T_3 = \frac{p_3 T_1 V_3}{p_1 V_1} = \frac{9 \times 10^6 \times 298}{115 \times 10^3} \times \frac{V_3}{V_1} = \frac{9 \times 10^6 \times 298}{115 \times 10^3} \times \frac{1}{18} = 1296 \text{ K}$$

Cut off ratio $= \beta = \dfrac{V_4}{V_3} = \dfrac{p_3 T_4}{p_4 T_3}$     but $p_4 = p_3$ so

$$\beta = \frac{T_4}{T_3} = \frac{2273}{1296} = \mathbf{1.75}$$

$$T_5 = T_4 \left( \frac{V_4}{V_5} \right)^{\gamma-1} \quad \text{but} \quad \frac{V_4}{V_5} = \frac{V_4}{V_3} \times \frac{V_3}{V_5} = \frac{1.75}{18} = 0.0974,$$

$$T_5 = 2273 \times 0.0974^{0.4} = \mathbf{895.6 \text{ K}}$$

$$Q_{\text{in}} = mc_p(T_4 - T_3) + mc_v(T_3 - T_2) \quad m = 1 \text{ kg}$$
$$= 1.005(2274 - 1296) + 0.718(1296 - 947) = 1232.5 \text{ kJ/kg}$$
$$Q_{\text{out}} = mc_v(T_5 - T_1)$$
$$= 0.718(895.6 - 298) = 429 \text{ kJ/g}$$
$$\eta = 1 - \frac{Q_{\text{out}}}{Q_{\text{in}}} = 1 - \frac{429}{1232} = 0.65 \text{ or } 65\%$$
$$W_{\text{net}} = Q_{\text{in}} \quad Q_{\text{out}} = 1232 - 429 = \mathbf{803 \text{ kJ/kg}}$$

## The diesel cycle

The diesel cycle precedes the dual combustion cycle. The diesel cycle is a reasonable approximation of what happens in slow-running engines such as large marine diesels. The initial accumulation of fuel and sharp detonation does not occur and the heat input is idealised as a constant pressure process only.

Again consider this cycle as being carried out inside a cylinder fitted with a piston. The p–V and T–s cycle diagrams are shown in Fig. 3.20.

**Fig. 3.20** *The Diesel cycle*

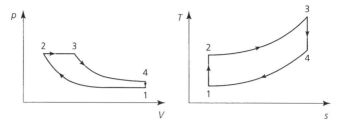

1–2 Reversible adiabatic (isentropic) compression.
2–3 Constant pressure heating.
3–4 Reversible adiabatic (isentropic) expansion.
4–1 Constant volume cooling.

$$\eta = 1 - \frac{Q_{out}}{Q_{in}} = 1 - \frac{mc_v(T_4 - T_1)}{mc_p(T_3 - T_2)} = 1 - \frac{(T_4 - T_1)}{\gamma(T_3 - T_2)}$$

The cycle is the same as the dual combustion cycle without the constant volume heating process. In this case, since $k = 1$, the efficiency is given by the formula:

$$\eta = 1 - \frac{\beta^\gamma - 1}{(\beta - 1)\gamma r_v^{\gamma-1}}$$

---

### WORKED EXAMPLE 3.7

An engine using the diesel cycle has a compression ratio of 20/1 and a cut off ratio of 2. At the start of the compression stroke the air is at 1 bar and 15 °C. Calculate:

1. The air standard efficiency of the cycle.
2. The maximum temperature in the cycle.
3. The heat input.
4. The net work output.

*Solution*
Initial data:

$\beta = 2$     $r_v = 20$     $\gamma = 1.4$     $c_v = 718$ J/kg K for air
$T_1 = 288$ K     $p_1 = 1$ bar.
The maximum temperature is $T_3$ and the maximum pressure is $p_3$ and $p_2$.

$$\eta = 1 - \frac{\beta^\gamma - 1}{(\beta - 1)\gamma r_v^{\gamma-1}} = 1 - \frac{2^{1.4} - 1}{(2 - 1) \times 1.4 \times 20^{0.4}}$$

$$= 1 - \frac{1.639}{1 \times 1.4 \times 3.314} = 0.647 \text{ or } \mathbf{64.7\%}$$

$$T_2 = T_1 r_v^{\gamma-1} = 288 \times 20^{0.4} = 954.5 \text{ K}$$

$$T_3 = \frac{V_2}{V_3} T_2 = \beta T_2 = 954.3 \times 2 = \textbf{1909 K}$$

$$Q_{in} = m c_p (T_3 - T_2) = 1.005(1909 - 954.5) = \textbf{959.3 kJ}$$

$$\eta = \frac{W_{net}}{Q_{in}} \qquad W_{net} = \eta Q_{in} = 0.647 \times 959.3 = \textbf{620.6 kJ}$$

## SELF-ASSESSMENT EXERCISE 3.5

Use $c_v = 0.718$ kJ/kg K, $c_p = 1.005$ kJ/kg K and $\gamma = 1.4$ throughout.

1. Draw p–V and T–s diagrams for a diesel cycle.

    The performance of a compression ignition engine is to be compared to the diesel cycle. The compression ratio is 16. The pressure and temperature at the beginning of compression are 1 bar and 15 °C respectively. The maximum temperature in the cycle is 1200 K. Calculate:
    (a) The cut off ratio.
    (b) The air standard efficiency.

2. A dual combustion cycle uses a compression ratio of 12/1. The cut off ratio is 2/1. The temperature and pressure before compression are 280 K and 1 bar respectively. The maximum temperature 2000 K. Calculate:
    (a) The thermal efficiency.
    (b) The nett work output per cycle per kg.

3. A dual combustion cycle uses a compression ratio of 20/1. The cut off ratio is 1.6/1. The temperature and pressure before compression are 30 °C and 1 bar respectively. The maximum cycle pressure is 100 bar. Calculate:
    (a) The maximum cycle temperature.
    (b) The thermal efficiency.
    (c) The nett work output per cycle per kg.

## 3.2.4 *Gas turbines*

A gas turbine engine normally burns fuel in the air that it uses as the working fluid. From this point of view it is an internal combustion engine that uses steady flow processes. Figure 3.21 shows a basic design.

The air is drawn in from atmosphere and compressed, which makes it hotter. The compressed air is blown into a combustion chamber in which fuel is burned, making it even hotter. This makes the volume increase. The hot air expands out of the chamber through a turbine, forcing it to revolve and produce power. The air becomes colder as it expands and eventually exhausts to atmosphere. The temperature drop over the turbine is larger than the temperature increase over the compressor. The turbine produces more power than is needed to drive the compressor, and nett power output is the result. In the

**Fig. 3.21** *The layout of a basic gas turbine engine*

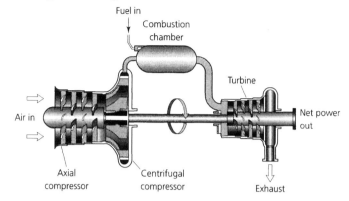

basic system, the turbine is coupled directly to the compressor and the power output is taken from the same shaft. The ideal air standard cycle is the Joule cycle.

### The Joule cycle

The Joule cycle is also known as the constant pressure cycle because the heating and cooling processes are conducted at constant pressure. This is the cycle used in a gas turbine engine, but it could conceivably be used in a closed system.

We can draw the layout in block diagram form as shown in Fig. 3.22.

**Fig. 3.22** *Symbolic representation of a basic gas turbine engine*

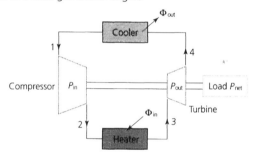

There are four ideal processes in the cycle.

1–2 Reversible adiabatic (isentropic) compression requiring power input.
$P_{in} = \Delta H/s = mc_p(T_2 - T_1)$
2–3 Constant pressure heating requiring heat input.
$\Phi_{in} = \Delta H/s = mc_p(T_3 - T_2)$
3–4 Reversible adiabatic (isentropic) expansion producing power output.
$P_{out} = \Delta H/s = mc_p(T_3 - T_4)$
4–1 Constant pressure cooling back to the original state requiring heat removal.
$\Phi_{out} = \Delta H/s = mc_p(T_4 - T_1)$

The pressure–volume and temperature–entropy diagrams are shown in Fig. 3.23.

**Fig. 3.23** *The Joule cycle*

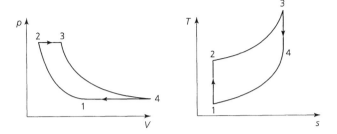

The efficiency is found by applying the first law of thermodynamics:

$$\Phi_{net} = P_{net}$$
$$\Phi_{in} - \Phi_{out} = P_{out} - P_{in}$$
$$\eta_{th} = \frac{P_{net}}{\Phi_{in}} = 1 - \frac{\Phi_{out}}{\Phi_{in}} = 1 - \frac{mc_p(T_4 - T_1)}{mc_p(T_3 - T_2)} = 1 - \frac{T_4 - T_1}{T_3 - T_2}$$

It assumed that the mass and the specific heats are the same for the heater and cooler.

It is easy to show that the temperature ratio for the turbine and compressor are the same.

$$\frac{T_2}{T_1} = \left(\frac{p_2}{p_1}\right)^{1-1/\gamma} = r_p^{1-1/\gamma} \qquad \frac{T_3}{T_4} = \left(\frac{p_3}{p_4}\right)^{1-1/\gamma} = r_p^{1-1/\gamma} \qquad \frac{T_3}{T_4} = \frac{T_2}{T_1}$$

where $r_p$ is the pressure compression ratio for the turbine and compressor.

$$\eta_{th} = 1 - \frac{T_4 - T_1}{T_3 - T_2} = 1 - \frac{(T_3 T_1/T_2) - T_1}{(T_2 T_4/T_1) - T_2} = 1 - \frac{T_1[(T_3/T_2) - 1]}{T_2[(T_4/T_1) - 1]}$$

$$\frac{T_3}{T_2} = \frac{T_4}{T_1} \qquad \frac{T_3}{T_2} - 1 = \frac{T_4}{T_1} - 1$$

$$\eta_{th} = 1 - \frac{T_1}{T_2} = 1 - \frac{T_4}{T_3} = 1 - \frac{1}{r_p^{1-1/\gamma}} = 1 - r_p^{-0.286} \quad \text{since } \gamma = 1.4$$

This shows that the efficiency depends only on the pressure ratio which in turn affects the hottest temperature in the cycle.

## WORKED EXAMPLE 3.8

A gas turbine uses the Joule cycle. The pressure ratio is 6/1. The inlet temperature to the compressor is 10 °C. The flow rate of air is 0.2 kg/s. The temperature at inlet to the turbine is 950 °C. Calculate:

1. The cycle efficiency.
2. The heat transfer into the heater.
3. The net power output.

$\gamma = 1.4 \qquad c_p = 1.005 \text{ kJ/kg K}$

*Solution*

$\eta_{th} = 1 - r_p^{-0.286} = 1 - 6^{-0.286} = 0.4$ or **40%**

$T_2 = T_1 r_p^{0.286} = 283 \times 6^{0.286} = 472.4$ K

$\Phi_{in} = mc_p(T_3 - T_2) = 0.2 \times 1.005 \times (1223 - 472.4) = $ **150.8 kW**

$\eta_{th} = \dfrac{P_{net}}{\Phi_{in}}$

$P_{net} = 0.4 \times 150.8 = $ **60.3 kW**

---

**SELF-ASSESSMENT EXERCISE 3.6**

γ = 1.4 and $c_p$ = 1.005 kJ/kg K throughout.

1.  A gas turbine uses the Joule cycle. The inlet pressure and temperature to the compressor are respectively 1 bar and −10 °C. After constant pressure heating, the pressure and temperature are 7 bar and 700 °C respectively. The flow rate of air is 0.4 kg/s. Calculate:
    (a) The cycle efficiency.
    (b) The heat transfer into the heater.
    (c) The net power output.

2.  A gas turbine expands draws in 3 kg/s of air from atmosphere at 1 bar and 20 °C. The combustion chamber pressure and temperature are 10 bar and 920 °C respectively. Calculate:
    (a) The Joule efficiency.
    (b) The exhaust temperature.
    (c) The nett power output.

3   A gas turbine draws in 7 kg/s of air from atmosphere at 1 bar and 15 °C. The combustion chamber pressure and temperature are 9 bar and 850 °C respectively. Calculate:
    (a) The Joule efficiency.
    (b) The exhaust temperature.
    (c) The nett power output.

# 3.3 Engine testing

On completion of this section you should be able to:

- Calculate the fuel power of an engine.
- Calculate the brake power of an engine.
- Calculate the indicated power of an engine.
- Calculate the various efficiencies of an engine.
- Calculate the mean effective pressure (MEP) of an engine.

## 3.3.1 *Fuel power*

Fuel power (FP) is the thermal power released by burning fuel inside the engine.

FP = mass of fuel burned per second × calorific value of the fuel.

$\quad = m_f \times CV$

All engines burn fuel to produce heat that is then partially converted into mechanical power. The chemistry of combustion is not dealt with here. The things you need to learn at this stage follow.

### Air/fuel ratio

This is the ratio of the mass of air used to the mass of fuel burned.

$\quad$ Air/Fuel Ratio $= m_a/m_f$

The ideal value that just completely burns all the fuel is called the **stoichiometric ratio**.

In reality, the air needed to ensure complete combustion is greater than the ideal ratio. This depends on how efficient the engine is at getting all the oxygen to meet the combustible elements. The volume of air drawn into the engine is theoretically equal to the capacity of the engine (the swept volumes of the cylinders). The mass contained in this volume depends upon the pressure and temperature of the air. The pressure in particular depends upon the nature of any restrictions placed in the inlet flow path.

### Calorific value

This is the heat released by burning 1 kg of fuel. There is a higher and lower value for fuels containing hydrogen. The lower value is normally used because water vapour formed during combustion passes out of the system and takes with it the latent energy.

---

### WORKED EXAMPLE 3.9

An engine consumes 0.01573 kg/s of air. The air/fuel ratio is 12/1. The calorific value is 46 MJ/kg. Calculate the fuel power.

*Solution*

Air consumed: $\quad m_a = 0.01573$ kg/s

Mass of fuel: $\quad m_f = 0.01573/12 = 0.00131$ kg/s

Heat released: $\quad$ FP = calorific value $\times m_f = 46\ 000$ kJ/kg $\times 0.00131$ kg/s

$\quad\quad\quad\quad\quad\quad = \textbf{60.3 kW}$

---

### SELF-ASSESSMENT EXERCISE 3.7

1. An engine consumes 43.1 g/s of air with an air/fuel ratio of 13/1. The calorific value is 45 MJ/kg. Calculate the heat released by combustion.

2. An engine requires 120 kW of fuel power by burning fuel with a calorific value of 37 MJ/kg. The air/fuel ratio required is 14/1. Calculate the mass flow rate of air required.

### 3.3.2 *Brake power*

Brake power (BP) is the output power of an engine measured by developing the power into a brake dynamometer on the output shaft. Dynamometers measure the speed and the torque of the shaft. The brake power is calculated with the formula

$$\text{BP} = 2\pi NT$$

where $N$ is the shaft speed in rev/s and $T$ is the torque in N m.

You may need to know how to work out the torque for different types of dynamometers. In all cases the torque is

$T = $ **net brake force** $\times$ **radius**

Figure 3.24 shows two types of dynamometer. The hydraulic dynamometer absorbs the engine power with an impeller inside a water-filled casing. Basically it is a pump with a restricted flow. The power heats up the water and produces a torque on the casing. The casing is restrained by a weight pulling down and a compression spring balance pushing down. The torque is then $(F + W) \times R$.

The drum type has a friction drum on which a belt rubs and absorbs the power by heating up the drum that is usually water cooled. A spring balance and one weight restrain the belt. The second equal weight acts to cancel out the other, so the torque is $F \times R$.

**Fig. 3.24**  *Two types of brake dynamometer*

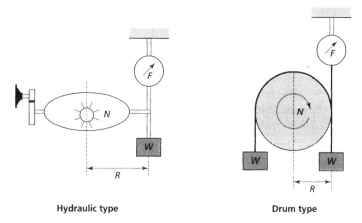

Hydraulic type                     Drum type

### 3.3.3 *Indicated power*

Indicated power (IP) is the power developed by the pressure of the gas acting on the pistons. It is found by recording the pressure against volume inside the cylinder. Such diagrams are called indicator diagrams and are taken with engine indicators. Modern indicators use transducers to measure the pressure and volume. This is processed electronically and displayed on a computer. Figure 3.25 shows a typical indicator diagram for an internal combustion engine.

**Fig. 3.25** *A typical indicator diagram for an engine*

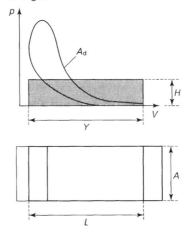

The average force on the piston throughout one cycle is $F$, where

$$F = \text{MEP} \times \text{area of piston} = p_m A$$

The mean effective pressure, $p_m$, is the mean pressure during the cycle.
The work done during one cycle is force × distance moved.

$$W = FL = p_m AL \quad (L \text{ is the stroke}).$$

The number of cycles per second is $N$. The indicated power is then

$$\text{IP} = p_m LAN \text{ per cylinder.}$$

Note that for a four-stroke engine $N =$ one-half of the shaft speed because the power cycle is performed every second revolution of the crank speed.

The MEP is found from the indicator diagram as follows. The area enclosed by the indicator diagram represents the work done per cycle per cylinder. Let this area be $A_d$ mm². The average height of the graph is $H$ mm. The length of the diagram is $Y$ mm. The shaded area is equal to $A_d$.

$$A_d = YH$$
$$H = A_d/Y$$

In order to convert $H$ into pressure units, the pressure scale (or spring rate) of the indicator measuring system must be known. Let this be $S_p$ kPa/mm. The MEP is then found as follows:

$$\text{MEP} = p_m = S_p H$$

This is also known as the indicated mean effective pressure (IMEP) because it is used to calculate the indicated power. There is also a brake mean effective pressure (BMEP). This is the mean pressure that would produce the brake power.

$$\text{BP} = (\text{BMEP})LAN$$
$$\text{BMEP} = \text{BP}/LAN$$

## 3.3.4 *Efficiencies*

### Brake thermal efficiency

This tells us how much of the fuel power is converted into brake power.

$$\eta_{BTh} = BP/FP$$

### Indicated thermal efficiency

This tells us how much of the fuel power is converted into brake power.

$$\eta_{ITh} = IP/FP$$

### Mechanical efficiency

This tells us how much of the indicated power is converted into brake power. The difference between them is due to frictional losses between the moving parts and the energy taken to run the auxiliary equipment, such as the fuel pump, water pump, oil pump and alternator.

$$\eta_{mech} = BP/IP$$

---

### WORKED EXAMPLE 3.10

A four-cylinder, four-stroke engine gave the following results on a test bed:

| | |
|---|---|
| Shaft speed | $N = 2500$ rev/min |
| Torque arm | $R = 0.4$ m |
| Net brake load | $F = 200$ N |
| Fuel consumption | $m_f = 2$ g/s |
| Calorific value | $CV = 42$ MJ/kg |
| Area of indicator diagram | $A_d = 300$ mm$^2$ |
| Pressure scale | $S_p = 80$ kPa/mm |
| Stroke | $L = 100$ mm |
| Bore | $D = 100$ mm |
| Base length of diagram | $Y = 60$ mm |

Calculate the BP, FP, MEP, IP, $\eta_{BTh}$, $\eta_{ITh}$ and $\eta_{mech}$.

*Solution*

BP $= 2\pi NT = 2\pi \times (2500/60) \times (200 \times 0.4) = $ **20.94 kW**

FP $= $ mass/s $\times CV = 0.002$ kg/s $\times 42\,000$ kJ/kg $= $ **84 kW**

IP $= pLAN$

    $p = $ MEP $= A_d/Y \times S_p = (300/60) \times 80 = $ **400 kPa**

    IP $= 400 \times 0.1 \times (\pi \times 0.1^2/4) \times (2500/60)/2$ per cylinder

       $= 6.54$ kW per cylinder

For 4 cylinders, IP $= 6.54 \times 4 = $ **26.18 kW**

    $\eta_{BTh} = 20.94/84 = $ **24.9%**

    $\eta_{ITh} = 26.18/84 = $ **31.1%**

    $\eta_{mech} = 20.94/26.18 = $ **80%**

1. A four-stroke spark ignition engine gave the following results during a test:

   | | |
   |---|---|
   | Number of cylinders | 6 |
   | Bore of cylinders | 90 mm |
   | Stroke | 80 mm |
   | Speed | 5000 rev/min |
   | Fuel consumption rate | 0.225 kg/min |
   | Calorific value | 44 MJ/kg |
   | Net brake load | 180 N |
   | Torque arm | 0.5 m |
   | Net indicated area | 720 mm$^2$ |
   | Base length of indicator diagram | 60 mm |
   | Pressure scale | 40 kPa/mm |

   Calculate:
   (a) The brake power.
   (b) The mean effective pressure.
   (c) The indicated power.
   (d) The mechanical efficiency.
   (e) The brake thermal efficiency.

2. A two-stroke spark ignition engine gave the following results during a test:

   | | |
   |---|---|
   | Number of cylinders | 4 |
   | Bore of cylinders | 100 mm |
   | Stroke | 100 mm |
   | Speed | 2000 rev/min |
   | Fuel consumption rate | 5 g/s |
   | Calorific value | 46 MJ/kg |
   | Net brake load | 500 N |
   | Torque arm | 0.5 m |
   | Net indicated area | 1500 mm$^2$ |
   | Base length of indicator diagram | 66 mm |
   | Pressure scale | 25 kPa/mm |

   Calculate:
   (a) The indicated thermal efficiency.
   (b) The mechanical efficiency.
   (c) The brake thermal efficiency.

3. A two-stroke diesel engine gave the following results during a test:

   | | |
   |---|---|
   | Number of cylinders | 4 |
   | Bore of cylinders | 80 mm |
   | Stroke | 80 mm |
   | Speed | 2200 rev/min |
   | Fuel consumption rate | 1.6 cm$^3$/s |
   | Fuel density | 750 kg/m$^3$ |
   | Calorific value | 60 MJ/kg |
   | Net brake load | 195 N |

| | |
|---|---|
| Torque arm | 0.4 m |
| Net indicated area | 300 mm² |
| Base length of indicator diagram | 40.2 mm |
| Pressure scale | 50 kPa/mm |

Calculate:
(a) The indicated thermal efficiency.
(b) The mechanical efficiency.
(c) The brake thermal efficiency.

4. A four-stroke diesel engine gave the following results during a test:

| | |
|---|---|
| Number of cylinders | 4 |
| Bore of cylinders | 90 mm |
| Stroke | 80 mm |
| Speed | 5000 rev/min |
| Fuel consumption rate | 0.09 kg/min |
| Calorific value | 44 MJ/kg |
| Net brake load | 60 N |
| Torque arm | 0.5 m |
| MEP | 280 kPa |

Calculate:
(a) The mechanical efficiency.
(b) The brake thermal efficiency.
(c) The indicated thermal efficiency.

# 3.4 Performance improvement

## 3.4.1 Internal combustion engines

In the preceding work it has been shown that the efficiency of internal combustion engines depends upon the volume/compression ratio, and for gas turbines it depends upon the pressure/compression ratio. This section debates some of the practical problems and solutions for improvement of performance.

**Engine management**
High compression ratios in spark ignition engines leads to pre-ignition as the fuel detonates without the aid of a spark before the point of maximum compression. This produces very high peaks of pressure and damages the engine. Reducing this problem involves the use of fuels that are less prone to detonate (high octane ratings). Timing of the spark ignition is also vital. The correct timing depends upon many factors such as air/fuel ratio and engine load. Modern engines use fuel management systems in which the timing and the air/fuel ratio are controlled by a computer connected to sensors. This allows greater compression ratios and hence efficiency.

Fuel injection gives a measure of control over the combustion process and this is now possible in petrol engines as well as in diesel engines.

## Turbocharging

The power produced by an engine basically depends on the amount of fuel burned. This is limited by the mass of air in the cylinder. To burn more fuel requires more air. Blowing air into the cylinders under pressure may do this and requires an air blower. This is a successful process in compression ignition engines but increases the problem of pre-ignition on spark ignition engines. The blower may be driven by a mechanical connection direct to the engine crankshaft. The Lobe compressor shown in Fig. 3.26 is commonly used. This arrangement is called **supercharging**. On large engines, the blower is driven by a small gas turbine that uses the exhaust from the engine to power it. This is called **turbocharging**. Figure 3.27 shows a turbocharger.

**Fig. 3.26** *A lobe type supercharger*

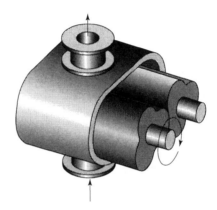

**Fig. 3.27** *A turbocharger*

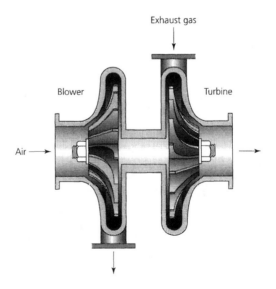

## Intercooling

The mass contained in a volume of air depends upon the temperature. The colder the air, the more mass it contains. Compressed air is naturally hot so if it can be cooled after compression, a greater mass of air may be supplied to the cylinder.

Turbocharging and intercooling on large compression ignition engines leads to improved efficiency as well as increased power. Figure 3.28 shows an intercooler designed to fit under a car radiator.

**Fig. 3.28**  *An intercooler for an automotive supercharger*

## 3.4.2 *Exhaust gas heat recovery*

When a large amount of hot exhaust gas is produced by either a gas turbine or a large diesel engine, the heat in the exhaust gas may be recovered for useful applications such as using it to produce hot water or steam in a boiler (Fig. 3.29). A factory might well use a gas turbine to produce electric power and hot water or steam. This is more economical than buying electricity.

**Fig. 3.29**  *A waste heat boiler coupled to a gas turbine*

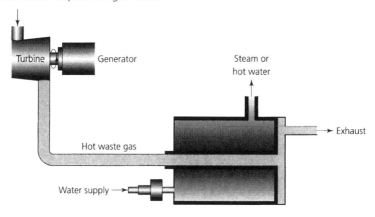

---

### SELF-ASSESSMENT EXERCISE 3.9

A factory is to be built that uses both electricity and steam. There are two options to be considered.

Option 1    Produce steam in an oil-fired boiler and purchase electricity.
Option 2    Generate electric power with a gas turbine and produce steam in a waste heat boiler using the exhaust gas.

---

## Operating data for steam boiler

Mass flow rate                    1 kg/s
Steam condition                   5 bar and dry saturated
Feed water temperature      15 °C.

When burning fuel, the combustion efficiency is typically 85%.

When using exhaust gas, the heat transfer from the gas may be assumed to be equal to the heat gained by the water and steam. The exhaust gas is cooled to 100 °C before leaving the boiler.

## Gas turbine data

Pressure ratio                                        7
Inlet air pressure                                    1 bar
Inlet air temperature                               15 °C
Combustion chamber temperature        1500 °C

## Fuel data

Any fuel to be burned in either the gas turbine or the boiler will be light oil with a calorific value of 42 MJ/kg.

- The cost of fuel is 12.7 p/kg.
- Electricity cost is 2.5 p/kWh (1 kWh = 3600 kJ)

Properties:   Air                          Burned gas
              $Cp = 1.005$ kJ/kg K     $Cp = 1.1$ kJ/kg K
              $\gamma = 1.4$           $\gamma = 1.3$

*Produce a report comparing the costs for both schemes. You will need to do the following tasks.*

## Steam boiler

Determine:

1. The energy required to make the steam.
2. The fuel required in kg/s.
3. The mass of exhaust gas required to produce the same steam in kg/s.

## Gas turbine

You will need to equate the heat transfer from burning fuel to the energy required to raise the temperature in the combustion chamber. Determine:

4. The mass flow of air.
5. The fuel burned in kg/s.
6. The power input of the compressor.
7. The power output of the turbine.
8. The nett power for generating electricity.

## Costing

Base the cost of Option 1 on the cost of fuel plus the cost of buying the same electricity as for Option 2. Base the cost of Option 2 on the cost of fuel only.

What other factors would you consider when making a decision on which option to take?

# **4** Air compressors

In order to complete this chapter you should be familiar with gas laws and polytropic gas processes. You will study the principles of reciprocating compressors in detail and some principles of rotary compressors. On completion of this chapter, you should be able to:

- Describe the working principles of reciprocating compressors.
- Describe the basic design of various other compressors.
- Define and calculate swept volume.
- Define and calculate volumetric efficiency.
- Define and calculate isothermal efficiency.
- Define and calculate indicated power.
- State the benefits of cooling.
- Calculate the heat rejected through cooling.
- Define and calculate the interstage pressures for multiple compressors.

Air is an expansive substance and dangerous when used at high pressures. For this reason, most applications are confined to items requiring low pressures (10 bar or lower) but there are industrial uses for high-pressure air up to 100 bar.

A compressor most commonly uses air. There are many types of compressors with different working principles and working conditions, of which the main types are:

- Reciprocating compressors.
- Sliding vane compressors.
- Lobe compressors.
- Helical screw compressors.
- Centrifugal compressors.
- Axial turbine compressors.

The function of all of them is to draw in air from the atmosphere and produce air at pressures substantially higher. Usually a storage vessel or receiver is used with the compressor.

Compressed air has many applications. It is also used for powering pneumatically operated machines. It is used as a power medium for workshop tools such as shown in Fig. 4.1.

**Fig. 4.1** *Examples of air tools*

Grinder                    Drill

# 4.1 Compressed air

### 4.1.1 *Atmospheric vapour*

Water vapour in the atmosphere has important consequences on compressors. Atmospheric air contains **water vapour** mixed with the other gases. The ratio of the mass of water vapour in the air to the mass of the air is called the **absolute humidity**. The quantity of water that can be absorbed into the air at a given pressure depends upon the temperature. The hotter the air, the more water it can absorb. When the air contains the maximum possible amount of vapour it is at its dew point and rain or fog will appear. The air is then said to have 100% humidity. When the air contains no water vapour at all (dry air), it has 0% humidity. This is called the **relative humidity**. For example if the air has 40% relative humidity it means that it contains 40% of the maximum that it could contain. There are various ways to determine the humidity of air and instruments for doing this are called **hygrometers**.

The importance of humidity to air compressors is as follows. When air is sucked into the compressor, it also takes in water vapour. When the air is compressed the pressure and temperature of the air increases, with the result that the compressed air will have a relative humidity of about 100% and it will be warm. When the air leaves the compressor it will cool down and the water vapour will condense. Water will then clog the compressor, the receiver and the pipes.

Water damages air tools, ruins paint sprays, and corrodes pipes and equipment. For this reason the water must be removed, and the best way to do this is to use a well-designed compressor installation and distribution network.

### 4.1.2 *Typical reciprocating compressor layout*

Figure 4.2 shows the layout of a two-stage reciprocating compressor typically for supplying a workshop.

### 4.1.3 *Hazards and safety*

Dangers associated with air compressors are as follows:

- Pressure vessels may rupture.
- Oil leaks may burn or cause other accidents.
- Oil in the compressed air may explode.
- Water in the compressed air may damage equipment.

**Fig. 4.2** *Typical layout of a two-stage compressor*

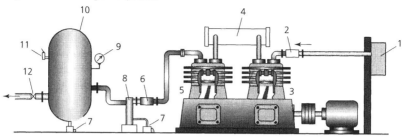

1. Induction box and silencer on outside of building with course screen
2. Induction filter
3. Low pressure stage
4. Intercooler
5. High-pressure stage
6. Silencer
7. Drain trap
8. After cooler
9. Pressure gauge
10. Air receiver
11. Safety pressure relief valve
12. Stop valve

There are many regulations concerning the use, maintenance and inspection of pressure vessels. Vessels must have their safe working pressure marked on them. They must have a pressure gauge and be fitted with an isolating valve. They must also be fitted with a pressure release valve to prevent overpressure.

In particular, if water accumulates in the cylinder of a reciprocating compressor, it may fill the space so completely that it prevents the piston reaching the end of its travel and cause damage to the piston and head.

Oil in the cylinder can explode during compression. Normally the operating pressure is not high enough to produce the temperature required. However, if the outlet becomes blocked (e.g. the valve sticks or the outlet pipe is closed with an isolating valve), then the danger exists.

Oil or water in the air can also cause damage when supplied to some kinds of tools. For this reason a good installation fully conditions the air to remove water, dirt and oil.

The following is a list of precautions to be taken against fire and explosions:

- Avoid overheating.
- Keep discharge temperatures within the recommended limits.
- Keep the deposit formation to a minimum by using the correct lubricant.
- Ensure efficient filtration of the air. This reduces wear on the valves and pistons and reduces deposits of carbonised particles.
- Avoid overfeeding oil to the cylinders.
- Minimise the carryover of oil between stages.
- Avoid high temperatures and low airflow when idling.
- Keep the coolers in good condition.
- Do not use solvents for cleaning; nor should they be used anywhere near an installation as the vapour given off can ignite.
- Do not allow naked flames (e.g. a burning cigarette) near an installation when it is opened.

### 4.1.4 *Free air delivery*

When a gas such as air flows in a pipe, the mass of the air depends upon the pressure and temperature. It would be meaningless to talk about the volume of the air unless the pressure and temperature are considered. For this reason the volume of air is usually stated as **free air delivery** or FAD. In other words, FAD refers to the volume the air would have if it was expelled from the pipe and returned to atmospheric pressure at the same temperature.

The FAD is also the volume of air drawn into a compressor from the atmosphere. After compression and cooling the air is returned to the original temperature, but is at a higher pressure. If we assume that atmospheric conditions are $p_a T_a$ and $V_a$ (the FAD) and the compressed conditions are $p$, $V$ and $T$, then applying the gas law we have:

$$\frac{pV}{T} = \frac{p_a V_a}{T_a} \qquad V_a = \frac{pVT_a}{Tp_a} = \text{FAD}$$

## 4.2 Cycle for reciprocating compressors

### 4.2.1 *Theoretical cycle*

Figure 4.3 shows the basic design of a reciprocating compressor. The piston reciprocates drawing in gas, compressing it and expelling it. If the piston expels all the air and there is no restriction at the valves, the pressure–volume cycle is as shown.

**Fig. 4.3** *Ideal model for a reciprocating compressor*

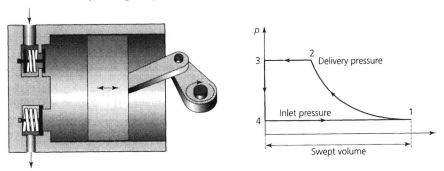

Gas is induced from 4 to 1 at the inlet pressure. It is then trapped inside the cylinder and compressed according the law $pV^n = C$. At point 2 the pressure reaches the same level as that in the delivery pipe and the outlet valve pops open. Air is then expelled at the delivery pressure. The delivery pressure might rise very slightly during expulsion if the gas is being compacted into a fixed storage volume. This is the way pressure builds up from switch on.

### 4.2.2 *Volumetric efficiency*

In reality, the piston cannot expel all the gas and a clearance volume is needed between the piston and the cylinder head. This means that a small volume of compressed gas is trapped in the cylinder at point 3. When the piston moves away from the cylinder head, the compressed gas expands by the law $pV^n = C$ until the pressure falls to the level of the inlet pressure. At point 4 the inlet valve opens and gas is drawn in. The volume drawn in from 4 to 1 is smaller than the swept volume because of this expansion.

**Fig. 4.4** *p–v diagram for a reciprocating compressor showing the effect of a clearance volume*

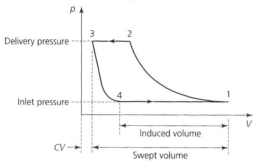

The volumetric efficiency is defined by the equation:

$$\eta_{vol} = \frac{\text{induced volume}}{\text{swept volume}}$$

It may be shown that this reduces to

$$\eta_{vol} = 1 - c\left[\left(\frac{p_2}{p_1}\right)^{(1/n)} - 1\right]$$

This efficiency is made worse if leaks occur past the valves or piston.

The clearance ratio is defined as

$$c = \frac{\text{clearance volume}}{\text{swept volume}}$$

Ideally the processes 2 to 3 and 4 to 1 are isothermal; that is to say, there is no temperature change during induction and expulsion.

---

**WORKED EXAMPLE 4.1**

Gas is compressed in a reciprocating compressor from 1 bar to 6 bar. The FAD is 13 dm³/s. The clearance ratio is 0.05. The expansion part of the cycle follows the law $pV^{1.2} = C$. The crank speed is 360 rev/min. Calculate the swept volume and the volumetric efficiency.

*Solution*

Swept volume = $V$    Clearance volume = $0.05V$

Consider the expansion from (3) to (4) on the $p$–$V$ diagram:

$$p_4 = 1 \text{ bar} \qquad p_3 = 6 \text{ bar} \qquad p_3 V_3^{1.2} = p_4 V_4^{1.2}$$
$$6(0.05V)^{1.2} = 1(V_4^{1.2})$$
$$\therefore \quad V_4 = 0.222V \text{ or } 22.2\% \text{ of } V$$

$$\text{FAD} = 0.013 \text{ m}^3/\text{s} \qquad V_1 = V + 0.05V = 1.05V$$
$$\text{Induced volume} = V_1 - V_4 = 1.05V - 0.222V = 0.828V$$
$$= 0.013 \text{ m}^3/\text{s}$$

$$\therefore \quad V = 0.013/0.828 = \mathbf{0.0157 \text{ m}^3/\text{s}}$$

Crank speed = 6 rev/s, so the swept volume = $0.0157/6 = 2.62 \text{ dm}^3$

$$\eta_{\text{vol}} = \frac{\text{induced volume}}{\text{swept volume}} = \frac{0.828V}{V} = \mathbf{82.8\%}$$

## WORKED EXAMPLE 4.2

Show that the volumetric efficiency of an ideal single-stage reciprocating compressor with a clearance ratio of $c$ is given by the expression.

$$\eta_{\text{vol}} = 1 - c\left[\left(\frac{p_H}{p_L}\right)^{1/n} - 1\right]$$

where $p_L$ is the inlet pressure and $p_H$ the outlet pressure.

**Solution**
Swept volume = $V_1 - V_3$     Induced volume = $V_1 - V_4$     Clearance volume = $V_3$

$$c = \frac{V_3}{V_1 - V_3} \qquad \therefore \quad V_1 - V_3 = \frac{V_3}{c} \tag{4.2.1}$$

$$\frac{V_1}{V_3} - 1 = \frac{1}{c} \qquad \therefore \quad \frac{V_1}{V_3} = \frac{1}{c} + 1 = \frac{1+c}{c} \tag{4.2.2}$$

$$\eta_{\text{vol}} = \frac{V_1 - V_4}{V_1 - V_3} \qquad \text{Substitute (4.2.1) for the bottom line}$$

$$= \frac{c(V_1 - V_4)}{V_3} = c\left(\frac{V_1}{V_3} - \frac{V_4}{V_3}\right) \qquad \text{Substitute (4.2.2)}$$

$$= c\left(\frac{1+c}{c} - \frac{V_4}{V_3}\right) = 1 + c - c\frac{V_4}{V_3}$$

$$\frac{V_4}{V_3} = \left(\frac{p_3}{p_4}\right)^{1/n} = \left(\frac{p_H}{p_L}\right)^{1/n}$$

$$\eta_{\text{vol}} = 1 + c - c\left(\frac{p_H}{p_L}\right)^{1/n} = 1 - c\left[\left(\frac{p_H}{p_L}\right)^{1/n} - 1\right]$$

A single-stage reciprocating compressor has a clearance volume of 20 cm$^3$. The bore and stroke are 100 mm and 80 mm respectively. The compression and expansion processes have a polytropic index of 1.25. The inlet and outlet pressures are 1 and 6 bar respectively. Determine the volumetric efficiency.

*Solution*

The swept volume is the product of stroke and bore area.

$$SV = 80 \times \frac{\pi \times 100^2}{4} = 628.3 \times 10^3 \text{ mm}^3 \text{ or } 628.3 \text{ cm}^3$$

The clearance volume is 20 cm$^3$.

$$c = \frac{20}{628.3} = 0.03183$$

$$\eta_{\text{vol}} = 1 - c\left[\left(\frac{p_H}{p_L}\right)^{1/n} - 1\right] = 1 - 0.03183\left[\left(\frac{6}{1}\right)^{1/1.25} - 1\right]$$

$$= 1 - 0.03183(4.192 - 1) = 1 - 0.1016 = \mathbf{0.898 \text{ or } 89.8\%}$$

### 4.2.3 *Real p–V diagrams*

In real compressors the warm cylinder causes a slight temperature rise over the induction from (4) to (1). The gas is restricted by the valves and $p_1$ is slightly less than $p_4$. The valves also tend to move so the real cycle looks more like Fig. 4.5.

**Fig. 4.5** *Realistic p–v diagram for a reciprocating compressor*

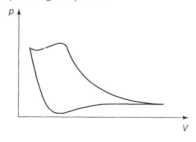

A single-stage reciprocating compressor produces a FAD of 2 dm$^3$/s at 420 rev/min. The inlet pressure is 1 bar. The polytropic index is 1.2 for the compression and expansion. The outlet pressure is 8 bar. The clearance volume is 10 cm$^3$. Determine the volumetric efficiency.

*Solution*

First find the induced volume. This is the free air drawn in for each revolution.

$$\text{FAD per rev} = \frac{2 \times 60}{420} = 0.2857 \text{ dm}^3/\text{rev}$$

This is the induced volume $V_1 - V_4$. The clearance volume is $V_3 = 10 \text{ cm}^3$ or 0.01 dm³ (given). Next we need to find $V_4$:

$$p_3 V_3^n = p_4 V_4^n \qquad 8 \times 0.01^{1.2} = 1 \times V_4^{1.2} \qquad \text{hence:} \quad V_4 = 0.0566 \text{ dm}^3$$
$$V_1 = 0.2857 + 0.0566 = 0.3423 \text{ m}^3$$

Swept volume $= V_1 - V_3 = 0.3323 \text{ dm}^3$

$$\eta_{\text{vol}} = \frac{V_1 - V_4}{V_1 - V_3} = \frac{0.2857}{0.3323} = \textbf{0.859 or 85.9\%}$$

## 4.2.4 *Indicated power*

The indicated work per cycle is the area enclosed by the $p$–$V$ diagram. The easiest way to find this is by integrating with respect to the pressure axis.

**Fig. 4.6** *Finding the indicated work for an ideal cycle*

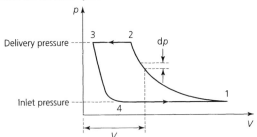

**Polytropic processes**

If the processes 1 to 2 and 3 to 4 are polytropic: $pV^n = C$ and $V = C^{1/n} p^{-1/n}$

The work done is given by $W = \int V \, dp$.

Consider the expression

$$\int V \, dp = C^{1/n} \int p^{-1/n} \, dp = \frac{C^{1/n} p^{1-1/n}}{1 - 1/n} = \frac{n}{n-1}(C^{1/n} p^{1-1/n})$$

$$C = pV^n \qquad \therefore \quad C^{1/n} = p^{1/n} V. \text{ Substitute in to make:}$$

$$\int V \, dp = \frac{nVp^{1/n} p^{1-1/n}}{n-1} = \frac{npV}{n-1}$$

Between the limits of $p_2$ and $p_1$ this becomes: $\quad W_{1-2} = \dfrac{n(p_2V_2 - p_1V_1)}{n-1}$

Between the limits $p_4$ and $p_3$ this becomes: $\quad W_{4-3} = \dfrac{n(p_4V_4 - p_3V_3)}{n-1}$

Subtract one from the other to find the indicated work.

$$W = \dfrac{n(p_2V_2 - p_1V_1)}{n-1} - \dfrac{n(p_3V_3 - p_4V_4)}{n-1}$$

$$= \dfrac{n}{n-1}\left\{p_1V_1\left[\left(\dfrac{p_2V_2}{p_1V_1} - 1\right) - p_4V_4\left(\dfrac{p_3V_3}{p_4V_4} - 1\right)\right]\right\}$$

Substitute the relationships $\quad \dfrac{V_2}{V_1} = \left(\dfrac{p_2}{p_1}\right)^{-1/n} \quad$ and $\quad \dfrac{V_3}{V_4} = \left(\dfrac{p_3}{p_4}\right)^{-1/n}$

$$W = \dfrac{n}{n-1}\left\{p_1V_1\left[\left(\dfrac{p_2}{p_1}\right)^{(n-1)/n} - 1\right] - p_4V_4\left[\left(\dfrac{p_3}{p_4}\right)^{(n-1)/n} - 1\right]\right\}$$

$$= \dfrac{n}{n-1}\{p_1V_1[r_\mathrm{p}^{(n-1)/n} - 1] - p_4V_4[r_\mathrm{p}^{(n-1)/n} - 1]\}$$

$$= \dfrac{n}{n-1}\{r_\mathrm{p}^{(n-1)/n} - 1\}(p_1V_1 - p_4V_4)$$

Since $p_1 = p_4$ we get

$$W = p_1\left(\dfrac{n}{n-1}\right)\{r_\mathrm{p}^{(n-1)/n} - 1\}(V_1 - V_4)$$

$$= p_1\left(\dfrac{n}{n-1}\right)\{r_\mathrm{p}^{(n-1)/n} - 1\}(\Delta V) \quad \text{where } \Delta V \text{ is the induced volume.}$$

The corresponding induced mass is $m = p_1\,\Delta V/RT_1$.

$$W = mRT_1\left(\dfrac{n}{n-1}\right)\{r_\mathrm{p}^{(n-1)/n} - 1\}$$

If the clearance volume is ignored, $\Delta V = V_1$.

$$W = \left(\dfrac{n}{n-1}\right)p_1V_1(r_\mathrm{p}^{(n-1)/n} - 1) \quad \text{or} \quad W = mRT_1\left(\dfrac{n}{n-1}\right)(r_\mathrm{p}^{(n-1)/n} - 1)$$

## Isothermal processes

If the processes (1) to (2) and (3) to (4) are isothermal, then: $\quad pV = C \quad$ and $\quad V = C'p^{-1}$.

The work done is given by $W = \int V\,\mathrm{d}p$

Consider the expression

$$\int V\,\mathrm{d}p = C\int p^{-1}\,\mathrm{d}p = C\ln p$$

Between the limits of $p_2$ and $p_1$ this becomes $\quad p_1 V_1 \ln\left(\dfrac{p_2}{p_1}\right)$

Between the limits $p_4$ and $p_3$ this becomes $\quad p_4 V_4 \ln\left(\dfrac{p_3}{p_3}\right)$

The indicated work (input) is then

$$W = p_1 V_1 \ln\left(\frac{p_2}{p_1}\right) - p_4 V_4 \ln\left(\frac{p_3}{p_4}\right)$$
$$= p_1 V_1 \ln(r_p) - p_4 V_4 \ln(r_p)$$
$$= \ln(r_p)(p_1 V_1 - p_4 V_4)$$

Since $p_1 = p_2$ we get

$$W = p_1 \ln(r_p)(V_1 - V_4) = p_1 \ln(r_p)\,\Delta V$$
$$= \ln(r_p)mRT_1$$

If the clearance volume is neglected, $\Delta V = V_1$

$$W = \ln(r_p)(p_1 V_1) = \ln(r_p)mRT_1$$

where $m$ is the mass induced and expelled each cycle and $W$ is the indicated work per cycle. The indicated power is found by multiplying $W$ by the strokes per second:

$$\text{IP} = W \times N \quad \text{where } N \text{ is the shaft speed in rev/s.}$$

### 4.2.5 *Isothermal efficiency*

The minimum indicated power is obtained when the index $n$ is a minimum. The ideal compression is hence isothermal with $n = 1$. The isothermal efficiency is defined as

$$\eta_{\text{iso}} = \frac{\text{isothermal work}}{\text{polytropic work}}$$
$$= \frac{p_1 \ln(r_p)(\Delta V)}{p_1[n/(n-1)]\{r_p^{(n-1)/n} - 1\}(\Delta V)}$$
$$= \frac{(n-1)\ln(r_p)}{n\{r_p^{(n-1)/n} - 1\}}$$

---

**WORKED EXAMPLE 4.5**

A single-stage reciprocating compressor draws in air at atmospheric pressure of 1.01 bar and delivers it at 9.5 bar. The polytropic index is 1.18 for the compression and expansion. The swept volume is 1.5 dm$^3$ and the clearance volume is 0.10 dm$^3$. The speed is 500 rev/min. Determine:

1. The volumetric efficiency.
2. The free air delivery.
3. The indicated power.
4. The isothermal efficiency.

---

## Solution

The clearance ratio is: $c = \dfrac{\text{clearance volume}}{\text{swept volume}} = \dfrac{0.1}{1.5} = 0.0667$

Pressure ratio is: $r_p = \dfrac{p_2}{p_1} = \dfrac{9.5}{1.01} = 9.406$

$$\eta_v = 1 - c(r_p^{1/n} - 1)$$
$$= 1 - 0.0667[(9.406^{1/1.18}) - 1] = 0.621$$

Induced volume $= \eta_v \times$ swept volume $= 0.621 \times 1.5 = \textbf{0.9315 dm}^3$

FAD per stroke = induced volume = 0.9318 dm$^3$
FAD per minute = $0.9315 \times 500 = 465.8$ dm$^3$/min or $\textbf{0.4658 m}^3\textbf{/s}$

Indicated power $= p_1\left(\dfrac{n}{n-1}\right)(r_p^{(n-1)/n} - 1) \times$ FAD

$$IP = 1.01 \times 10^5 \left(\dfrac{1.18}{0.18}\right)(9.406^{0.18/1.18} - 1) \times \dfrac{0.4658}{60}$$
$$= 5141.3(9.406^{0.1525} - 1)$$
$$= 5141.3(1.407 - 1) = \textbf{2096 W}$$

$$\eta_{iso} = \dfrac{(n-1)\ln(r_p)}{n(r_p^{(n-1)/n} - 1)} = \dfrac{0.18 \ln 9.406}{1.18(9.406^{0.18/1.18} - 1)} = \dfrac{0.3419}{0.407} = \textbf{0.84}$$

---

## SELF-ASSESSMENT EXERCISE 4.1

1. A reciprocating air compressor operates between 1 bar and 8 bar. The clearance volume is 15 cm$^3$ and the swept volume is 900 cm$^3$. The index of compression and expansion is 1.21. Calculate:
   (a) The ideal volumetric efficiency.
   (b) The ideal indicated work per cycle.
   (c) The isothermal work per cycle.
   (d) The isothermal efficiency.

2. A reciprocating air compressor following the ideal cycle has a free air delivery of 60 dm$^3$/s. The clearance ratio is 0.05. The inlet is at atmospheric pressure of 1 bar. The delivery pressure is 7 bar and the compression is polytropic with an index of 1.3. Calculate:
   (a) The ideal volumetric efficiency.
   (b) The ideal indicated power.
   (c) The isothermal efficiency.

3. A single-stage reciprocating compressor draws in air at atmospheric pressure of 1.0 bar and delivers it at 12 bar. The polytropic index is 1.21 for the compression and expansion. The swept volume is 2.0 dm$^3$ and the clearance volume is 0.16 dm$^3$. The speed is 600 rev/min. Determine:
   (a) The ideal volumetric efficiency.    (c)   The ideal indicated power.
   (b) The free air delivery.                     (d)   The isothermal efficiency.

## 4.3 Multiple-stage compressors

The main advantage to compressing the air in stages is that the air may be cooled between each stage and the overall compression is nearer to being isothermal. This reduces the power requirement and allows removal of water from the air. Two-stage compression is common, but when very high pressure is required, more stages may be used.

### 4.3.1 The effect of intercooling on the indicated work

Consider the $p$–$V$ diagram for a compressor with two stages, as shown in Fig. 4.7. Stages 1 to 4 form a normal cycle conducted between $p_L$ and $p_M$. The air is expelled during process 3 to 4 at $p_M$ and constant temperature. The air is then cooled at the intermediate pressure which causes a contraction in the volume, making the induced volume $V_8$ to $V_5$ smaller than the expelled volume $V_2$ to $V_3$. The high-pressure cycle is then a normal cycle conducted between $p_M$ and $p_H$.

The shaded area of the diagram represents the work saved by using the intercooler.

**Fig. 4.7** *p–v diagram for a two-stage reciprocating compressor*

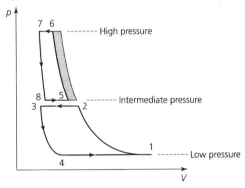

### 4.3.2 Optimal interstage pressure

The optimal saving is obtained by choosing the correct intermediate pressure, which may be found as follows:

$$W = W_1 + W_2$$

where $W_1$ is the work done in the low-pressure stage and $W_2$ is the work done in the high-pressure stage.

$$W = \frac{mRn(T_2 - T_1)}{n - 1} + \frac{mRn(T_6 - T_5)}{n - 1}$$

Since $T_2 = T_1(p_2/p_1)^{1-1/n}$ and $T_6 = T_5(p_6/p_5)^{1-1/n}$, then assuming the same value of $n$ for each stage:

$$W = mR\left[\frac{nT_1}{n-1}\left(\frac{p_2}{p_1}\right)^{1-1/n} - 1\right] + mR\left[\frac{nT_6}{n-1}\left(\frac{p_6}{p_5}\right)^{1-1/n} - 1\right]$$

Since $p_2 = p_5 = p_\text{m}$, $p_6 = p_\text{H}$ and $p_1 = p_\text{L}$:

$$W = mR\left[\frac{nT_1}{n-1}\left(\frac{p_\text{M}}{p_\text{L}}\right)^{1-1/n} - 1\right] + mR\left[\frac{nT_6}{n-1}\left(\frac{p_\text{H}}{p_\text{M}}\right)^{1-1/n} - 1\right]$$

For a minimum value of $W$ we differentiate with respect to $p_\text{M}$ and equate to zero.

$$\frac{\text{d}W}{\text{d}p_\text{M}} = mRT_1 p_\text{L}^{(1-n)/n} p_\text{M}^{-1/n} - mRT_5 p_\text{H}^{(n-1)/n} p_\text{M}^{(1-2n)/n}$$

If the intercooler returns the air to the original inlet temperature so that $T_1 = T_5$, then equating to zero reveals that for minimum work

$$p_\text{M} = (p_\text{L} p_\text{H})^{1/2}$$

It can further be shown that when this is the case, the work done by both stages is equal. When $K$ stages are used, the same process reveals that the minimum work is done when the pressure ratio for each stage is $(p_\text{L}/p_\text{H})^{1/K}$.

## 4.4 Rotary compressors

Figure 4.8 shows three types of rotary compressor: vane type, centrifugal type and axial flow type; Figure 4.9 shows a screw compressor.

**Fig. 4.8** *Vane, centrifugal and axial flow compressors*

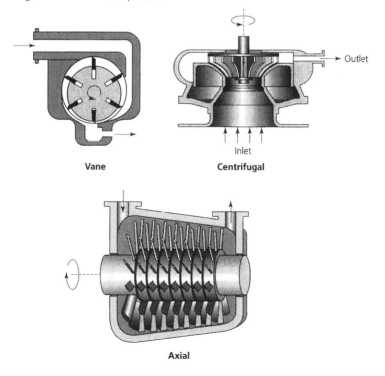

**Vane**   **Centrifugal**

**Axial**

### 4.4.1 *Vane compressor*

The vanes fit in slots in the rotor, which is eccentric to the bore of the cylinder. When the rotor is turned, centrifugal force throws the vanes out against the wall of the cylinder. The space between the vanes grows and shrinks as the rotor turns, so if inlet and outlet passages are cut in the cylinder at the appropriate point, air is drawn in, squeezed and expelled.

This type of compressor is suitable for small portable applications and is relatively cheap.

Vane compressors often use oil to lubricate and cool the air and a system similar to that shown for the screw compressor (Fig. 4.9) is used.

### 4.4.2 *Centrifugal compressor*

The rotor has a set of vanes shaped as shown in Fig. 4.8. When the rotor spins, the air between the vanes is thrown outwards by centrifugal force and gathered inside the casing. As the air slows down in the casing, the kinetic energy is converted into pressure. The shape of the casing is important and is basically an eccentric passage surrounding the rotor edge. Fresh air is drawn in from the front of the rotor.

Centrifugal compressors are suitable for medium and large flow rates. Pressures up to 25 bar may be obtained by using several stages or using them as the second stage of an axial flow type. Very large compressors are used to supply large volumes of air at low pressure to combustion chambers and blast furnaces.

### 4.4.3 *Axial flow compressor*

The axial flow compressor is basically many rows of fan blades arranged along the axis. Each row gives the air kinetic energy. Figure 4.8 does not show the fixed vanes in between each row that slow the air down again and raise the pressure. In this way the pressure gradually increases as the air flows along the axis from inlet to outlet. Often a centrifugal stage is situated at the end in order to give it a boost and change the direction of flow to the side. Typical industrial compressors can provide 70 m$^3$/s at 15 bar. They are not suitable for small flow rates (below 15 m$^3$/s).

Axial flow compressors are commonly used in jet and gas turbine engines but they have many applications where large flow rates and medium to high pressure are required.

### 4.4.4 *Screw compressor*

In this type of compressor, two rotors have helical lobes cut on them in such a way that when they mesh and rotate in opposite directions, air is drawn along the face of the lobes from input to output. Oil is used liberally to seal the air. The oil also acts as a coolant and Fig. 4.9 shows how the oil and air are separated and cooled in a radiator. The oil is recirculated.

**Fig. 4.9** *Layout of a screw compressor showing the cooling system used*

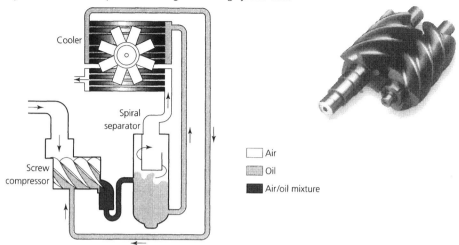

### 4.4.5 *Lobe compressor*

Lobe compressors are commonly used as superchargers on large engines. The basic design can be seen in Fig. 3.26 (page 86). Air is carried around between the lobes and the outer wall and is expelled when the lobes come together. These compressors are not suitable for high pressures but flow rates around 10 000 m³/h are achievable.

## 4.5 Coolers

Coolers are used for the following reasons:

● To reduce the indicated work in multiple-stage compressors.
● To condense water from the air.

For reciprocating compressors, the cooling takes place in the following places:

● The cylinder.
● Between stages.
● After final compression.

### 4.5.1 *Cylinder cooling*

The cylinders may be cooled with air and are designed with cooling fins on the outside. Circulating water through a cooling jacket produces more effective cooling.

### 4.5.2 *Intercoolers*

These are usually simple heat exchangers with water cooling. Drain traps are fitted to them to remove the water that condenses out of the air. Indicated work is saved, as explained in section 4.3.1.

Assuming that no heat is lost to the surroundings, the first law may be applied to the air and water sides of the equation to produce the following heat balance:

$$\Phi = m_a c_a \, \Delta T_a = m_w c_w \, \Delta T_w$$

where $m_a$ is the mass flow rate of air; $m_w$ is the mass flow rate of water; $\Delta T_a$ is the temperature change of the air; $\Delta T_w$ is the temperature change of the water; $c_a$ is the specific heat capacity of air; and $c_w$ is the specific heat capacity of water.

## 4.5.3 *Aftercoolers*

The only purpose of an aftercooler is to cool the air to around ambient conditions and condense water from the air. This is usually another water-cooled heat exchanger and the same heat balance may be applied.

---

**WORKED EXAMPLE 4.6**

A single acting reciprocating compressor runs at 360 rev/min, takes in air at 1 bar and 15 °C and compresses it in three stages to 64 bar. The free air delivery is 0.0566 m³/s. There is an intercooler between each stage, which returns the air to 15 °C. Each stage has one piston with a stoke of 100 mm. Calculate:

1. The ideal pressure between each stage.
2. The ideal indicated power per stage.
3. The heat rejected from each cylinder.
4. The heat rejected from each intercooler.
5. The isothermal efficiency.
6. The swept volume of each stage.
7. The bore of each cylinder.

Ignore leakage and the effect of the clearance volume. The index of compression is 1.3 for all stages.

*Solution*
Pressure ratio for each stage $= (64/1)^{1/3} = 4$; hence the pressure after stage 1 is

$$1 \times 4 = 4 \text{ bar}$$

The pressure after the second stage is $4 \times 4 = 16$ bar; hence the final pressure is

$$16 \times 4 = 64 \text{ bar}$$
$$T_1 = 288 \text{ K} \qquad m = p_1 V/RT_1 = (1 \times 10^5) \times 0.0566/(287 \times 288) = 0.06847 \text{ kg/s}$$
$$T_2 = 288(4)^{0.3/1.3} = 396.5 \text{ K}$$

The indicated power for each stage is the same, so this will be calculated for the first stage:

$$\text{IP} = mRnT_1[(p_2/p_1)^{(1-1/n)} - 1]/(n - 1) \quad \text{since } m \text{ is the mass compressed}$$
$$= 0.06847 \times 287 \times 1.3 \times 288(4^{0.3/1.3} - 1)/(1.3 - 1) = \mathbf{9.246 \text{ kW}}$$

## Cylinder cooling

Consider the energy balance over the first stage (Fig. 4.10).

**Fig. 4.10** *Cylinder cooling on a reciprocating compressor*

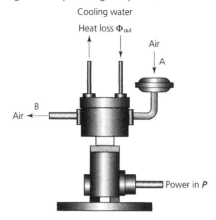

Balancing the energy we have:

$$H_A + P_{in} = H_B + \Phi_{out}$$
$$\Phi_{out} = P_{in} - mc_p(T_B - T_A) = 9.246 - 0.06847 \times 1.005(396.5 - 288)$$
$$= \mathbf{1.78 \ kW} \text{ (rejected from each cylinder)}$$

## Intercooler

Now consider the intercooler (Fig. 4.11). No work is done and the temperature is cooled from $T_2$ to $T_5$.

$$\Phi_{out} = mc_p(T_C - T_D) = 0.0687 \times 1.005(396.5 - 288) = 7.49 \ kW$$

**Fig. 4.11** *Design of a simple intercooler*

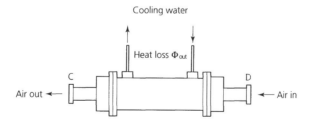

## Isothermal efficiency

The ideal isothermal power $= mRT_1 \ln (p_1/p_2)$ per stage.

$$P_{iso} = 0.06847 \times 287 \times 288 \ln 4 = 7.846 \ kW$$
$$\eta_{iso} = 7.846/9.246 = 84.9\%$$

## Swept volumes

Consider the first stage. The FAD is 0.0566 m³/s. In the ideal case where the air is drawn in at constant temperature and pressure from the atmosphere, the FAD is given by

FAD = swept volume × speed   (speed = 6 rev/s)

If the clearance volume is ignored, the FAD gives the swept volume:

SV (1st stage) = 0.0566/6 = 0.00943 m³
= bore area × stroke
$0.00943 = (\pi D^2/4) \times 0.1$;   hence:   $D_1 = 0.347$ m

Now consider the second stage. The air is returned to atmospheric temperature at inlet with a pressure of 4 bar. The volume drawn is hence 1/4 of the original FAD. The swept volume of the second stage is hence

0.00943/4 = 0.00236 m³
$0.00236 = (\pi D^2/4) \times 0.1$;   hence:   $D_2 = 0.173$ m

By the same reasoning the swept volume of the third stage is

0.00943/16 = 0.000589 m³
$0.000589 = (\pi D^2/4) \times 0.1$;   hence:   $D_3 = 0.0866$ m

## SELF-ASSESSMENT EXERCISE 4.2

1. A two-stage compressor draws in 8 m³/min from atmosphere at 15 °C and 1.013 bar. The air is compressed with an index of compression of 1.27 to the interstage pressure of 6 bar. The intercooler must cool the air back to 15 °C. (Look up the appropriate mean value of $c_p$ in your tables.) Calculate the heat that must be extracted from the air in kW.

2 A single-acting two-stage compressor draws in 8.5 m³/min of free air and compresses it to 40 bar. The compressor runs at 300 rev/min. The atmospheric conditions are 1.013 bar and 15 °C. There is an intercooler between stages that cools the air back to 15 °C. The polytropic index for all compressions is 1.3. The volumetric efficiency is 90% for the low-pressure stage and 85% for the high-pressure stage. Calculate:
   (a) The intermediate pressure for minimum indicated work.
   (b) The theoretical indicated power for each stage.
   (c) The heat rejected in each cylinder.
   (d) The heat rejected by the intercooler.
   (e) The swept volumes of both stages.

3. A two-stage reciprocating air compressor works between pressure limits of 1 and 20 bar. The inlet temperature is 15 °C and the polytropic index is 1.3. Intercooling between stages reduces the air temperature back to 15 °C. Both stages have the same stroke. Neglect the effect of the clearance volume.

Calculate:
(a) The free air delivery for each kWh of indicated work.
(b) The mass of air that can be compressed for each kWh of indicated work.
(c) The ratio of the cylinder diameters.
(*Note*: 1 kWh = 3.6 MJ)

4. A single-acting compressor draws in atmospheric air at 1 bar and 15 °C. The air
   is compressed in two stages to 9 bar. The compressor runs at 600 rev/min. The
   installation has an intercooler that reduces the air temperature to 30 °C at inlet
   to the second stage. The polytropic index for all compressions is 1.28. The
   clearance volume for each stage is 4% of the swept volume. The low-pressure
   cylinder is 300 mm diameter and the stroke for both stages is 160 mm.
   Calculate:
   (a) The optimal interstage pressure.
   (b) The volumetric efficiency of each stage.
   (c) The free air delivery.
   (d) The induced volume of the high pressure stage.
   (e) The diameter of the high pressure cylinder.
   (f) The indicated power for each stage.

# 5 Steam and gas turbines

When you have completed this chapter, you should be able to:

- Explain the basic design principles of turbines.
- Explain the Carnot steam cycle.
- Explain the basic steam power cycle.
- Describe improvements to the Rankine cycle.
- Describe the basic gas turbine power cycle.
- Describe advanced gas turbine power cycles.
- Solve problems concerning steam and gas turbine power plant.

## 5.1 Turbine design

### 5.1.1 A brief history

- **120 BC: Hero of Alexandria** constructs a simple reaction turbine. This was constructed from a spherical vessel with two spouts as shown in Fig. 5.1. Heat turned the water inside into steam that escaped through the spouts and made the vessel rotate.
- **1629: Branca**, an Italian, created the first impulse turbine (Fig. 5.1). Steam issuing from a nozzle struck the vanes on a wheel and made it revolve.

**Fig. 5.1** *Turbines designed by Branca and Hero*

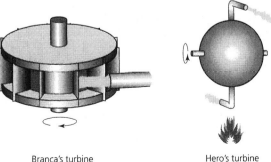

Branca's turbine            Hero's turbine

- **Windmills**, developed in medieval times, formed the main source of power for centuries.
- **1884: Charles Parsons** developed the first practical reaction turbine. This machine developed around 7 kW of power.
- **1889: De Laval** developed the first practical impulse turbine capable of producing around 2 kW of power.

Others who developed the impulse turbine were **Rateau** in France and **Curtis** in the USA.

## 5.1.2 *Impulse theory*

Turbines are generally classified as either *impulse* or *reaction*. This refers to the type of force acting on it and causing it to rotate.

**Impulsive forces** are exerted on an object when it diverts or changes the flow of a fluid passing over it. A very basic impulse turbine is the windmill, which converts the kinetic energy of the wind into mechanical power.

Consider a rotor with vanes arranged around the edge (Fig. 5.2). Fluid is directed at the vanes by a set of nozzles.

**Fig. 5.2**  *A simple turbine wheel*

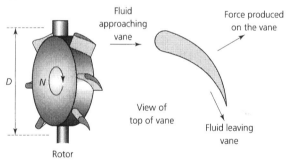

If there is no pressure drop in the process, the resulting force on the vanes is entirely due to the change in the momentum of the fluid and the force is entirely impulsive. It is of interest to note that the name 'impulsive' comes from Newton's second law of motion:

Impulse = change in momentum

Impulsive force = rate of change in momentum

$$F = m \, \Delta v$$

where $m$ is the mass flow rate in kg/s and $\Delta v$ is the change in velocity of the fluid. This is a vector quantity and may be applied to any direction. If we make $\Delta v$ the change in velocity in the direction of motion we obtain the force making the rotor turn. This direction is usually called the *whirl direction* and $\Delta v_w$ means the change in velocity in the whirl direction:

$$F = m \, \Delta v_w$$

If we assume that the vanes are rotating on a mean circle of diameter $D$ at $N$ rev/s, then the linear velocity of the vanes will be $u$ m/s. This is given by the equation:

$$u = \pi D N$$

The power produced by any moving force is the product of force and velocity. The power of the ideal rotor is given by the equation:

$$P = m\,\Delta v_w u = m\,\Delta v_w \pi N D$$

This is the fundamental way of finding the power produced by fluids passing over moving vanes. In order to find the vector quantity $\Delta v_w$, we draw vector diagrams for the velocities. For this reason, the power is called **diagram power**:

$$\text{diagram power} = m\,\Delta v_w \pi N D$$

The construction of the vector diagrams for fluids flowing over vanes is not covered in this book and you should refer to more advanced text if you wish to study it at a deeper level.

## WORKED EXAMPLE 5.1

The vanes on a simple steam turbine are mounted on a rotor with a mean diameter of 0.6 m. The steam flows at a rate of 0.8 kg/s and the velocity in the whirl direction is changed by 80 m/s. The turbine rotates at 600 rev/min. Calculate the diagram power.

*Solution*

| | |
|---|---|
| Rotor speed: | $N = 600/60 = 10$ rev/s |
| Velocity of the vanes: | $u = \pi N D = \pi \times 10 \times 0.6 = 18.85$ m/s |
| Diagram power: | $DP = mu\,\Delta v_w = 0.8 \times 18.85 \times 80 = 1206.5$ W |

A practical impulse turbine needs several sets of moving vanes and fixed vanes, as shown in Fig. 5.3. The fixed vanes act as nozzles that convert pressure into velocity. The steam from the nozzles is deflected by the moving row. There is a pressure drop over each fixed row.

**Fig. 5.3** *Vane configuration for an impulse turbine*

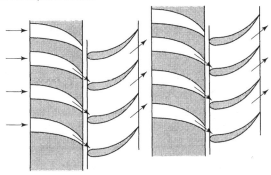

### 5.1.3 *Reaction theory*

Reaction forces are exerted on an object when it causes the velocity of the fluid to change. Consider a simple nozzle in which the fluid accelerates due to the change in the cross-sectional area (Fig. 5.4). The kinetic energy of the fluid increases, and since energy is conserved, the pressure of the fluid drops. In other words, the pressure behind the fluid forces it through the nozzle causing it to speed up. The force required to accelerate the fluid is in the direction of the acceleration. Every force has an equal and opposite reaction, so an equal and opposite force is exerted on the nozzle. This is the principle used in rockets.

**Fig. 5.4**  *A nozzle*

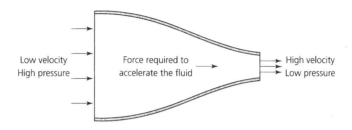

Low velocity High pressure — Force required to accelerate the fluid — High velocity Low pressure

It should be borne in mind that steam and gas, unlike liquid, undergo a volume increase when the pressure falls. It is thus possible to accelerate steam and gas without narrowing the flow passage.

The force required to accelerate the fluid is given by the equation:

$$F = m\,\Delta v$$

The reaction force acting on the nozzle is equal and opposite in direction.

Figure 5.5 shows the layout of the blades for a turbine that uses both reaction and impulse. The fixed rows accelerate the steam and there is a pressure drop over the row. The moving row also accelerates the steam and there is a further pressure drop over the moving row. The blades are thus moved by both impulse and reaction forces. If the rows of blades are identical, the pressure drop over each is the same and there is 50% impulse and 50% reaction.

**Fig. 5.5**  *Vane configuration for a combined reaction and impulse turbine*

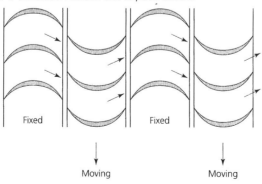

Fixed          Fixed

Moving          Moving

The moving vanes experience both reaction and impulsive forces and the two together is given by the change in momentum. The formula developed in section 5.1.2 applies to any kind of turbine.

Diagram power = $m \, \Delta v_w \pi ND$

## Axial force

The change in momentum that produces the force on the blade is not only in the direction of rotation. There is also a change of velocity and hence momentum in the direction of the axis of rotation and this pushes the turbine rotor in that direction. This would require a large thrust bearing in the turbine design, but this can be avoided by placing two identical rotors back to back, which cancels out the axial thrust. Figure 5.6 shows the schematic for such an arrangement.

**Fig. 5.6** *Symbolic representation of a back to back turbine layout*

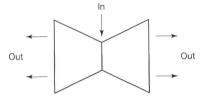

Because the volume of the steam or gas increases greatly as it progresses along the axis, the height of the blades increases in order to accommodate it. Figure 5.7 shows a turbine with the casing removed. There are three sets or cylinders each with double flow. The exhaust steam has such a large volume that entry to the condenser is through the large passages underneath. The condenser occupies the space below the turbine hall. Figure 5.8 shows the rotor of a large steam turbine.

**Fig. 5.7** *Photograph of a power station turbine set with the case removed*

**Fig. 5.8** *Photograph of steam turbine rotor*

## 5.2 Steam cycles

### 5.2.1 *The Carnot steam cycle*

In Chapter 2 you learned that a Carnot cycle gave the highest thermal efficiency possible for an engine working between two temperatures. The cycle consisted of isothermal heating and cooling and reversible adiabatic expansion and compression.

Consider a cycle that uses vapour throughout. Evaporation and condensation at constant pressure is also at constant temperature, and isothermal heating and cooling is therefore theoretically possible. The cycle would consist of the same four processes as before, but each process would be carried out in a separate steady flow plant item with the vapour flowing from one to the other in a closed loop, as shown in Fig. 5.9.

The four processes are:

1–2   Evaporation at constant pressure and temperature requiring heat input.
2–3   Reversible adiabatic expansion in the turbine giving power output.
3–4   Cooling and condensing at constant pressure and temperature in the condenser requiring heat output.
4–1   Reversible adiabatic compression requiring power input.

**Fig. 5.9** *Symbolic representation of a Carnot steam cycle*

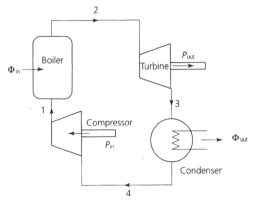

In order that no temperature changes occur in the evaporator and condenser, the vapour must be wet at inlet and outlet. Overcooling will produce liquid at temperatures below the saturation temperature and overheating will superheat it beyond the saturation temperature. The cycle will be a rectangle on the *T–s* diagram and, as shown, on the *h–s* diagram.

**Fig. 5.10** *H–s and t–s diagram for a Carnot steam cycle*

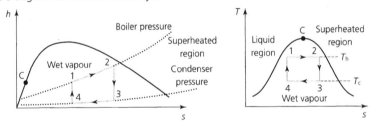

## SELF-ASSESSMENT EXERCISE 5.1

1. A steam turbine has its vanes on a mean diameter of 1.2 m and rotates at 1500 rev/min. The change in the velocity of whirl is 65 m/s and the change in the axial velocity is 20 m/s. The flow rate is 1 kg/s. Calculate:
   (a) The diagram power.
   (b) The axial force.

2. A steam turbine is to be designed to rotate at 3000 rev/min and produce 5 kW of power when 1 kg/s is used. The vanes will be placed on a mean diameter of 1.4 m. Calculate the change in the velocity of whirl that will have to be produced.

3. A gas turbine has rotor blades on a mean diameter of 0.5 m and the rotor turns at 2000 rev/min. The change in the whirl velocity is 220 m/s and the diagram power is 2 MW. Calculate the mass flow rate of gas.

The limits are that at point 2 it may be dry saturated vapour but not superheated. At point 1 it may be saturated water but not undercooled. If these limits are not used, then the vapour has a dryness fraction at each point. Since heat transfer only occurs at the evaporator and condenser, the heat transfer rates are given by the expressions:

$$\Phi_{in} = m(h_2 - h_1) = T_h \, \Delta S \quad \text{(Boiler)}$$
$$\Phi_{out} = m(h_3 - h_4) = T_c \, \Delta S \quad \text{(Condenser)}$$

where $T_h$ is the boiler temperature and $T_c$ is the condenser temperature. The thermal efficiency may be found from the first law:

$$\eta_{th} = 1 - (\Phi_{out}/\Phi_{in}) = 1 - (T_c/T_h)$$

This expression is the same as for the gas version (Chapter 2).

### WORKED EXAMPLE 5.2

A Carnot cycle is conducted on steam as follows. The evaporator produces dry saturated steam at 10 bar. The steam is expanded reversibly and adiabatically in a turbine to 1 bar. The exhaust steam is partially condensed and then compressed back to 10 bar. As a result of the compression, the wet steam is changed completely into saturated water.

1. Assuming a flow rate of 1 kg/s throughout, determine the condition and specific enthalpy at each point in the cycle.
2. Calculate the energy transfers for each stage.
3. Show that the efficiency is correctly predicted by the expression $\eta_{th} = 1 - T_{cold}/T_{hot}$

*Solution*
We will refer to the previous diagrams throughout.

*Evaporator*
$h_2 = h_g$ at 10 bar (since it is dry saturated) = 2778 kJ/kg
$s_2 = s_g$ at 10 bar (since it is dry saturated) = 6.586 kJ/kg K
$h_1 = h_f$ at 10 bar (since it is saturated water) = 763 kJ/kg

$\Phi_{in} = 1(2778 - 763) = \textbf{2015 kW}$

*Turbine*
Since the expansion is isentropic, $s_2 = s_3 = 6.586$ kJ/kg K

$s_3 = 6.586 = s_f + x_3 s_{fg}$ at 1 bar
$\quad\quad = 1.303 + x_3(6.056);\quad$ hence: $\quad x_3 = 0.872$
$h_3 = h_f + x_3 h_{fg}$ at 1 bar = 417 + (0.872)(2258) = 2387 kJ/kg

$P_{out} = 1(2778 - 2387) = \textbf{391.2 kW}$

## Compressor

Since the compression is isentropic, $s_4 = s_1$

$s_1 = s_f$ at 10 bar (since it is saturated water) = 2.138 kJ/kg K

$s_4 = s_1 = 2.138 = s_f + x_4 s_{fg}$ at 1 bar
$$= 1.303 + x_4(6.056); \quad \text{hence:} \quad x_4 = 0.138$$
$h_4 = h_f + x_4 h_{fg}$ at 1 bar $= 417 + (0.139)(2258) = 728.3$ kJ/kg

Power input $= 1(763 - 728.3) = \textbf{34.7 kW}$

## Condenser

Heat output $= 1(2387 - 728.3) = 1658.7$ kW

Energy balances rounded off to nearest kW:

Total energy input $= 34.7 + 2015 = 2050$ kW
Total energy output $= 391.2 + 1658.7 = 2050$ kW
Net power output $= 391.2 - 34.7 = 356$ kW
Net heat input $= 2015 - 1658.7 = 356$ kW
Thermal efficiency $= P_{net}/\Phi_{in} = 356/2015 = 17.7\%$
$$= 1 - \Phi_{out}/\Phi_{in} = 1 - 1658.7/2015 = \textbf{17.7\%}$$

The hottest temperature in the cycle is $t_s$ at 10 bar = **179.9 °C or 452.9 K**
The coldest temperature in the cycle is $t_s$ at 1 bar = **99.6 °C or 372.6 K**

The Carnot efficiency $= 1 - 372.6/452.9 = \textbf{17.7\%}$

---

### SELF-ASSESSMENT EXERCISE 5.2

1. A steam power plant uses the Carnot cycle. The boiler puts 25 kW of heat into the cycle and produces wet steam at 300 °C. The condenser produces wet steam at 50 °C. Calculate:
   (a) The efficiency of the plant.
   (b) The net power output.
   (c) The heat removed by the condenser.

2. A steam power plant is based on the Carnot cycle. The boiler is supplied with saturated water at 20 bar and produces dry saturated steam at 20 bar. The condenser operates at 0.1 bar. Assuming a mass flow rate of 1 kg/s, calculate:
   (a) The thermal efficiency.
   (b) The power output of the turbine.
   (c) The heat transfer rate into the boiler.

## 5.2.2 The Rankine cycle

The Rankine cycle is a practical cycle and most steam power plants are based on it (Fig. 5.11). The problems with the Carnot cycle are as follows:

---

- It produces only small net power outputs for the plant size because dry saturated steam is used at inlet to the turbine.
- It is impractical to compress wet steam because the water content separates out and fills the compressor.
- It is impractical to control the condenser to produce wet steam of the correct dryness fraction.

In order to resolve these problems, the Rankine cycle uses superheated steam from the boiler to the turbine. The condenser completely condenses the exhaust steam into saturated water. The compressor is replaced with a water (feed) pump to return the water to the boiler. This results in reduced efficiency but greater quantities of power.

**Fig. 5.11** *Symbolic representation of a Rankine steam cycle*

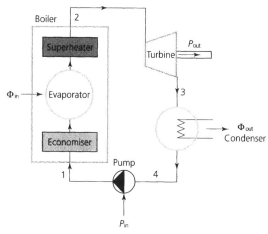

The plant layout is shown in Fig. 5.11. First let's briefly examine the boiler.

## Boiler

For reasons of combustion efficiency (which you do not have to study), a practical boiler is made up of three sections.

- **Economiser**  This is a water heater inside the boiler that raises the water temperature at the boiler pressure to just below the saturation temperature at that pressure.
- **Evaporator**  This unit usually consists of a drum and tubes in which the water is evaporated and the steam is driven off.
- **Superheater**  This is a heater placed in the hottest part of the boiler. It raises the temperature of the steam well beyond the saturation temperature.

There are many boiler designs, but not all of them have these features. The main point is that a heat transfer rate is needed into the boiler unit in order to heat up the water, evaporate it and superheat it. The overall heat transfer is

$$\Phi_{in} = m(h_2 - h_1)$$

Let us now look at some other practical aspects of a steam power plant.

## Extraction pump and hotwell

In a practical steam cycle the condensate in the condenser is extracted with an extraction pump and the water produced is the coldest point in the steam cycle. This is usually placed into a vessel where it can be treated and extra water added to make up for leaks. This point is called the **hotwell** because it contains hot water. The main feed pump returns this water to the boiler at high pressure (Fig. 5.12). In the following diagrams, extraction pumps and hotwells are not shown.

**Fig. 5.12**  *Feed water circuit for a steam plant showing a hotwell*

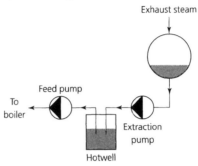

Now let us examine the cycle with the aid of property diagrams.

**Fig. 5.13**  *H–s and T–s diagram for a Rankine steam cycle*

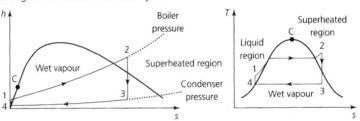

The process 4 to 1 is cramped into the corner of the *h–s* diagram and is not clear.

### *Boiler* (process 1 to 2: heat input)

The water at point 1 is below the saturation temperature at the boiler pressure. The economiser first heats it up raising the temperature, enthalpy and entropy until it reaches the saturation curve. The water is then evaporated and, finally, the temperature is raised by superheating the steam to point 2:

$$\Phi_{in} = m(h_2 - h_1)$$

### *Turbine* (process 2 to 3: power output)

The second process is the expansion in the turbine, which is ideally reversible and adiabatic and is represented by a vertical line on Fig. 5.13.

$$P_{out} = m(h_2 - h_3)$$

Turbines in real plant are often in several stages and the last stage is specially designed to cope with water droplets in the steam that becomes wet as it gives up its energy. You must use the isentropic expansion theory in order to calculate the dryness fraction and enthalpy of the exhaust steam.

### Condenser (process 3 to 4: heat output)
The third process is the condenser where the wet steam at point 3 is ideally turned into saturated water at the lower pressure (point 4). Condensers usually work at very low pressures (vacuums) in order to make the turbine give maximum power. The heat removed is given by

$$\Phi_{out} = m(h_3 - h_4)$$

Since the condenser produces condensate (saturated water), $h_4 = h_f$ at the condenser pressure.

### Pump (process 4 to 1: power input)
The final process which completes the cycle is the pumping of the water (point 4) from the low condenser pressure to the boiler at high pressure (point 1). In reality there are many things which are done to the feed water before it goes back into the boiler and the pressure is often raised in several stages. For the Rankine cycle we assume one stage of pumping which is adiabatic and the power input to the pump is

$$P_{in} = m(h_1 - h_4)$$

The power required to pump the water is much less than that required to compress the vapour (if it was possible). The power input to the feed pump is very small compared to the power output of the turbine and you can often neglect it altogether. In this case we assume that $h_1 = h_4$.

If you are not ignoring the power input, then you need to find $h_1$. If you know the exact temperature of the water at inlet to the boiler (outlet from the pump) then you may be able to look it up in tables. The nearest approximation is to look up $h_f$ at the water temperature. Since the water is at high pressure, this figure will not be very accurate and you may correct it by adding the flow energy. We will look at this in greater detail later. Let's first do a simple example with no great complications.

---

### WORKED EXAMPLE 5.3

A steam power plant is based on the Rankine cycle. The steam produced by the boiler is at 40 bar and 400 °C. The condenser pressure is 0.035 bar. Assume isentropic expansion. Ignore the energy term at the feed pump.

Calculate the Rankine cycle efficiency and compare it to the Carnot efficiency for the same upper and lower temperature limits.

*Solution*

**Fig. 5.14**  *Cycle layout*

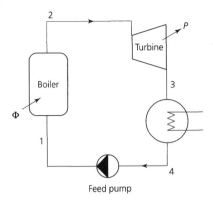

*Turbine*
$h_2 = 3214$ kJ/kg at 40 bar and 400 °C.
Since the expansion is isentropic then

$$s_2 = 6.769 \text{ kJ/kg K} = s_3 = 0.391 + 8.13x \quad (x = 0.785)$$
$$h_3 = h_f + xh_{fg} = 112 + 0.785(2438) = 2024.6 \text{ kJ/kg}$$

*Condenser*

$$h_4 = h_f \text{ at } 0.035 \text{ bar} = 112 \text{ kJ/kg}$$

*Boiler*
If the power input to the pump is neglected, then

$$h_4 = h_1 = 112 \text{ kJ/kg}$$
$$\Phi_{in} = h_2 - h_1 = 3102 \text{ kJ/kg.}$$
$$P_{out} = h_2 - h_3 = 1189.4 \text{ kJ/kg}$$
$$\eta = P/\Phi_{in} = 38.3\%$$

*Carnot efficiency*
The hottest temperature in the cycle is 400 °C (673 K) and the coldest temperature
is $t_s$ at 0.035 bar, and this is 26.7 °C (299.7 K).
The Carnot efficiency is $1 - 299.7/673 =$ **55.5%**, which is higher as expected.

Let us now examine the feed pump in more detail.

*Feed pump*
When water is compressed its volume hardly changes. This is the important factor that
is different from the compression of a gas. Because the volume hardly changes, the
temperature should not increase and the internal energy does not increase. The steady

flow energy equation would then tell us that the power input to the pump is virtually equal to the increase in flow energy. We may write

$$P_{in} = mv\, \Delta p$$

Since the volume of water in nearly all cases is 0.001 m³/kg, this becomes

$$P_{in} = 0.001m\, \Delta p = 0.001m(p_1 - p_2)$$

If we use pressure units of bars, then

$$P_{in} = 0.001m(p_1 - p_2) \times 10^5 \text{ W}$$

Expressed in kilowatts, this is

$$P_{in} = m(p_1 - p_2) \times 10^{-1} \text{ kW}$$

From this we may also deduce the enthalpy of the water after the pump:

$$P_{in} = m(h_1 - h_4)$$

Hence $h_1$ may be deduced.

---

### WORKED EXAMPLE 5.4

Repeat Worked Example 3, but this time do not ignore the feed pump and assume that the boiler inlet condition is unknown.

*Solution*

$$P_{in} = 1 \text{ kg/s } (40 - 0.035) \times 10^{-1} = 4 \text{ kW}$$
$$4 = 1 \text{ kg/s } (h_1 - h_4) = (h_1 - 112)$$
$$h_1 = 116 \text{ kJ/kg}$$

Reworking the energy transfers gives

$$\Phi_{in} = h_2 - h_1 = 3214 - 116 = 3098 \text{ kJ/kg}$$
$$P_{net} = P_{out} - P_{in} = 1189.4 - 4 = 1185.4 \text{ kJ/kg}$$
$$\eta = P_{net}/\Phi_{in} = 1185.4/3098 = \textbf{38.3\%}$$

Notice that the answers are not noticeably different from those obtained by ignoring the feed pump.

### WORKED EXAMPLE 5.5

A steam power plant uses the Rankine cycle, with the following details:

| | |
|---|---|
| Boiler pressure | 100 bar |
| Condenser pressure | 0.07 bar |
| Temperature of steam leaving the boiler | 400 °C |
| Mass flow rate | 55 kg/s |

Calculate the cycle efficiency, the net power output and the specific steam consumption.

### Solution

**Turbine**

$h_2 = 3097$ kJ/kg at 100 bar and 400 °C.

For an isentropic expansion we find the ideal condition at point 3 as follows:

$s_2 = 6.213$ kJ/kg K $= s_3 = 0.559 + 7.715x_3$ $\quad (x_3 = 0.733)$
$h_3 = h_f + x_3 h_{fg} = 163 + 0.733(2409) = 1928$ kJ/kg
$P_{out} = m(h_2 - h_3) = 55(3097 - 1928) = 64.3$ MW

**Condenser**

$h_4 = h_f$ at 0.07 bar $= 163$ kJ/kg
$\Phi_{out} = m(h_3 - h_4) = 55(1928 - 163) = 97.1$ MW

**Pump**
Ideal power input = flow energy change = $mv(\Delta p)$

$P_{in} = 55(0.001)(100 - 0.07) \times 10^5 = 550$ kW
$\quad = m(h_1 - h_4) = 55(h_1 - 163)$; hence: $h_1 = 173$ kJ/kg

**Boiler**

$\Phi_{in} = m(h_2 - h_1) = 55(3097 - 173) = 160.8$ MW

**Efficiency**

$P_{net} = P_{out} - P_{in} = 64.3 - 0.55 = 63.7$ MW
$\eta = P_{net}/\Phi_{in} = 63.7/160.8 =$ **39.6%**

Alternatively: $\quad P_{net} = \Phi_{in} - \Phi_{out} = 160.8 - 97.1 =$ **63.7 MW**
This should be the same as $P_{net}$ since the net energy entering the cycle must equal the net energy leaving.

$\eta = 1 - \Phi_{out}/\Phi_{in} = 1 - 97.1/160.8 =$ **39.6%**

**Specific steam consumption**
This is given by:

SSC $= P_{net}/\text{mass flow} = 63.78/55 =$ **1.159 MW/kg/s** or MJ/kg

---

### SELF-ASSESSMENT EXERCISE 5.3

1. A simple steam plant uses the Rankine cycle with the following data:

| | |
|---|---|
| Flow rate | 45 kg/s |
| Boiler pressure | 50 bar |
| Steam temperature from boiler | 300 °C |
| Condenser pressure | 0.07 bar |

Assuming isentropic expansion and pumping, determine:
(a) The power output of the turbine.
(b) The power input to the pump.
(c) The heat input to the boiler.
(d) The heat rejected in the condenser.
(e) The thermal efficiency of the cycle.

2. A simple steam power plant uses the Rankine cycle with the following data:

| | |
|---|---|
| Flow rate | 3 kg/s |
| Boiler pressure | 100 bar |
| Steam temperature from boiler | 600 °C |
| Condenser pressure | 0.04 bar |

Assuming isentropic expansion and pumping, determine:
(a) The power output of the turbine.
(b) The power input to the pump.
(c) The heat input to the boiler.
(d) The heat rejected in the condenser.
(e) The thermal efficiency of the cycle.

3. (a) Explain why practical steam power plants are based on the Rankine cycle rather than the Carnot cycle.
   (b) A simple steam power plant uses the Rankine cycle with the following data:

| | |
|---|---|
| Boiler pressure | 15 bar |
| Steam temperature from boiler | 300 °C |
| Condenser pressure | 0.1 bar |
| Net power output | 1.1 MW |

Calculate:
(i) The cycle efficiency.
(ii) The steam flow rate.

# 5.3 Rankine cycle variations

If an industry needs sufficient quantities of process steam (e.g. for sugar refining) and electric power, it becomes economical to use the steam for both purposes. This is done with a steam turbine and generator and the process steam is obtained in two ways as follows:

- By exhausting the steam at the required pressure (typically 2 bar) to the process instead of to the condenser. A turbine designed to do this is called a **back-pressure turbine**.
- By bleeding steam from an intermediate stage in the expansion process. A turbine designed to do this is called a **pass-out turbine**.

The steam cycle is standard except for these modifications.

## 5.3.1 *Back-pressure turbines*

Back-pressure turbines are designed to operate with a back pressure, unlike normal turbines that operate with a vacuum at the exhaust. Figure 5.15 shows the basic circuit.

**Fig. 5.15** *Symbolic representation of a back-pressure steam cycle*

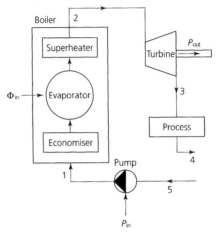

**WORKED EXAMPLE 5.6**

For a steam circuit as shown previously, the boiler produces superheated steam at 50 bar and 400 °C. This is expanded isentropically to 3 bar. The exhaust steam is used for a process. The returning feed water, at 1 bar and 40 °C, is pumped to the boiler. The water leaving the pump is at 40 °C and 50 bar. The net power output of the cycle is 60 MW. Calculate the mass flow rate of the steam.

*Solution*
Referring to the previous cycle sketch for location points we find

$$h_2 = 3196 \text{ kJ/kg} \qquad s_2 = 6.646 \text{ kJ/kg K}$$

For an ideal expansion

$$s_1 = s_2 = 6.646 = s_f + x s_{fg} \text{ at 3 bar}$$
$$6.646 = 1.672 + x(5.321)$$
$$\therefore x = 0.935$$

$$h_4 = h_f + x h_{fg} \text{ at 3 bar}$$
$$= 561 + 0.935(2164)$$
$$= 2584 \text{ kJ/kg}$$

Change in enthalpy = $2584 - 3196 = -612 \text{ kJ/kg}$

The power output of the turbine is found from the steady flow energy equation, so

$P = m(-612)$ kW $= -612m$ kW (output)

Next we examine the enthalpy change at the pump:

$h_1 = 168$ kJ/kg at 1 bar and 40 °C
$h_2 = 172$ kJ/kg at 50 bar and 40 °C.

Change in enthalpy $= 172 - 169 = 3$ kJ/kg
The power input to the pump is found from the steady flow energy equation, so:

$P = -m(3)$ kW $= -3m$ kW (input)

Net power output of the cycle $= 60$ MW; hence

$60\ 000 = 612m - 3m$
$\therefore\quad m = \textbf{98.5 kg/s}$

---

## SELF-ASSESSMENT EXERCISE 5.4

1. A steam cycle is performed as follows. The boiler produces 3 kg/s of superheated steam at 60 bar and 400 °C. The steam is supplied to a turbine that expands it isentropically and with no friction to 1.5 bar. The exhaust steam is supplied to a process. The feed water is supplied to the pump at 1.013 bar and 100 °C and delivered to the boiler at 60 bar. The pump may be considered as ideal. Calculate:
   (a) The power output of the turbine.
   (b) The heat input to the boiler.
   (c) The power input to the pump.
   (d) The thermal efficiency of the cycle.

2. A back-pressure steam cycle works as follows. The boiler produces 8 kg/s of steam at 40 bar and 500 °C. This is expanded isentropically to 2 bar. The pump is supplied with feed water at 0.5 bar and 30 °C and delivers it to the boiler at 31 °C and 40 bar. Calculate:
   (a) The net power output.
   (b) The heat input to the boiler.
   (c) The thermal efficiency of the cycle.

## 5.3.2 *Pass-out turbines*

The circuit of a simple pass-out turbine plant is shown in Fig. 5.16. Steam is extracted between stages of the turbine for process use. The steam removed must be replaced by make-up water at point 6.

In order to solve problems you need to study the energy balance at the feed pumps more closely so that the enthalpy at inlet to the boiler can be determined. Consider the pumps on their own, as in Fig. 5.17.

**Fig. 5.16** *Symbolic representation of a pass-out steam cycle*

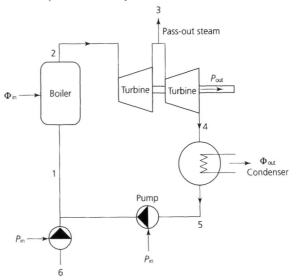

**Fig. 5.17** *Feed pump arrangement*

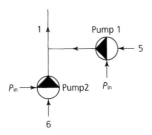

The balance of power is:

$$P_1 + P_2 = \text{increase in enthalpy per second}$$
$$= m_1 h_1 - m_6 h_6 - m_5 h_5$$

From this the value of $h_1$ or the mass $m$ may be determined. This is best shown with a worked example.

---

**WORKED EXAMPLE 5.7**

The circuit in Fig. 5.18 shows the information normally available for a feed pump circuit. Determine the enthalpy at entry to the boiler.

*Solution*
If no other details are available, the power input to the pump is $mv\,\Delta p$. Assume that $v = 0.001$ m³/kg.

---

**Fig. 5.18** *Feed pump details*

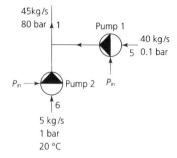

$P = mv \, \Delta p = m \times 0.001 \times \Delta p \text{ (bar)} \times 10^5 \times 10^{-3} = m \, \Delta p \times 10^{-1} \text{ kW}$

Pump 1:  $P_1 = mv \, \Delta p = (40)(80 - 0.1)(10^{-1}) = 319.6 \text{ kW}$

Pump 2:  $P_2 = mv \, \Delta p = (5)(80 - 1)(10^{-1}) = 39.5 \text{ kW}$

Total power input $= 319.6 + 39.5 = 359.1 \text{ kW}$

$h_5 = h_f = 192 \text{ kJ/kg at 0.1 bar}$

$h_6 = 84 \text{ kJ/kg (from water tables or approximately } h_f \text{ at 20 °C)}$

Balancing energy we obtain:

$359.1 = 45h_1 - 40h_5 - 5h_6$
$\qquad = 45h_1 - 40(192) - 5(84)$
$h_1 = \textbf{188 kJ/kg}$

## WORKED EXAMPLE 5.8

A pass-out turbine plant works as shown in Fig. 5.16. The boiler produces steam at 60 bar and 500 °C and this is expanded through two stages of turbines. The first stage expands to 3 bar where 4 kg/s of steam is removed. The second stage expands to 0.09 bar. Assume that the expansion is a straight line on the $h$–$s$ chart.

The condenser produces saturated water. The make-up water is supplied at 1 bar and 20 °C. The net power output of the cycle is 40 MW. Calculate:

1. The flow rate of steam from the boiler.
2. The heat input to the boiler.
3. The thermal efficiency of the cycle.

*Solution*

*Turbine expansion*

$h_2 = 3421 \text{ kJ/kg from tables}$

$h_3 = 2678 \text{ kJ/kg using isentropic expansion and entropy}$

$h_4 = 2166 \text{ kJ/kg using isentropic expansion and entropy}$

These results may be obtained from the $h$–$s$ chart (Fig. 5.19).

**Fig. 5.19** *Isentropic expansion on a h–s diagram*

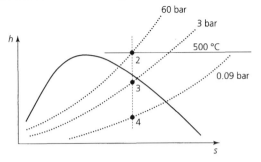

### Power output

$$P_{out} = m(h_3 - h_2) + (m - 4)(h_3 - h_4)$$
$$= m(3421 - 2678) + (m - 5)(2678 - 2166)$$
$$= 743m + 512m - 2760$$

### Power input
The power input is to the two feed pumps (Fig. 5.20).

**Fig. 5.20** *Feed pump details*

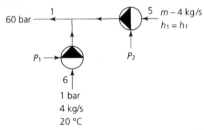

$h_6 = 84$ kJ/kg (water at 1 bar and 20 °C)
$h_5 = h_f$ at 0.09 bar = 183 kJ/kg.

$$P_1 = mv\,\Delta p = 4 \times (60 - 1) \times 10^{-1} = 23.6 \text{ kW}$$
$$P_2 = mv\,\Delta p = (m - 4) \times (60 - 0.09) \times 10^{-1} = 5.99m - 23.96 \text{ kW}$$

### Net power

$$40\,000 \text{ kW} = P_{out} - P_1 - P_2$$
$$= 743m + 512m - 2560 - 23.6 - 5.99m + 23.96$$
$$= 1251m - 2560; \quad \text{hence:} \quad m = \textbf{34 kg/s}$$

### Energy balance on pumps

$P_1 = 23.6$ kW
$P_2 = 179.8$ kW (using the value of $m$ just found)

$$mh_1 = (m - 4)h_5 + P_1 + P_2$$
$$34h_1 = 30 \times 183 + 23.6 + 179.8$$
$$h_1 = 167.5 \text{ kJ/kg}$$

*Heat input*

$$\Phi_{in} = m(h_2 - h_1) = \textbf{110 680 kW}$$

*Efficiency*

Efficiency $= \eta = 40/110.7 = \textbf{36\%}$

## SELF-ASSESSMENT EXERCISE 5.5

1. A steam turbine plant is used to supply process steam and power. The plant comprises an economiser, boiler, superheater, turbine, condenser and feed pump. The process steam is extracted between intermediate stages in the turbine at 2 bar pressure. The steam temperature and pressure at outlet from the superheater are 500 °C and 70 bar respectively. The turbine exhausts at 0.1 bar. The make-up water is at 15 °C and 1 bar and it is pumped into the feed line to replace the lost process steam. Assume that the expansion is isentropic.

    If due allowance is made for the feed pump work, the net mechanical power delivered by the plant is 30 MW when the process steam load is 5 kg/s. Sketch clear *T–s* and *h–s* and flow diagrams for the plant, and calculate:
    (a) The flow rate of steam flow leaving the superheater.
    (b) The rate of heat transfer to the boiler.

2. An industrial plant requires 60 MW of process heat using steam at 2.6 bar which it condenses to saturated water. This steam is derived from the intermediate stage of a turbine that produces 30 MW of power to drive the electric generators. The steam is raised in boilers and supplied to the turbines at 80 bar pressure and 600 °C. The steam is expanded isentropically to the condenser pressure of 0.05 bar. Calculate:
    (a) The flow rate of the steam bled to the process.
    (b) The flow rate of the steam from the boiler.

## 5.3.3 *Reheating*

Steam reheating is another way of improving the thermodynamic efficiency by attempting to keep the steam temperature more constant during the heating process (Fig. 5.21).

Superheated steam is first passed through a high-pressure turbine. The exhaust steam is then returned to the boiler to be reheated almost back to its original temperature. The steam is then expanded in a low-pressure turbine. In theory, many stages of turbines and reheating could be done, thus making the heat transfer in the boiler more isothermal and hence more reversible and efficient.

**Fig. 5.21** *Symbolic representation of a reheat cycle*

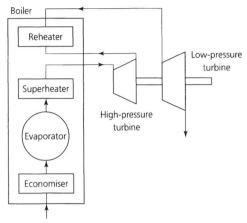

## 5.3.4 *Feed heating*

Feed heating is another way of improving the efficiency of a steam power plant. The feed water returning to the boiler is heated nearer to the saturation temperature with steam bled from the turbines at appropriate points. There are two types.

- Indirect contact.
- Direct contact.

### Indirect contact

The steam does not mix with the feed water at the point of heat exchange. The steam is condensed through giving up its energy and the hot water resulting may be inserted into the feed system at the appropriate pressure.

### Direct contact

The bled steam is mixed directly with the feed water at the appropriate pressure and condenses and mixes with the feed water. Figure 5.22 shows a basic plant with a single feed heater added.

**Fig. 5.22** *Symbolic representation of a cycle with a regenerative feed heater*

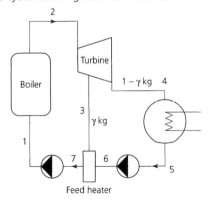

If a steam cycle used many stages of regenerative feed heating and many stages of reheating, the result would be an efficiency similar to that of the Carnot cycle. Although practicalities prevent this happening, it is quite normal for an industrial steam power plant to use several stages of regenerative feed heating and one or two stages of reheating. This produces a significant improvement in the cycle efficiency.

There are other features in advanced steam cycles that further improve the efficiency and are necessary for practical operation; for example, air extraction at the condenser, steam recovery from turbine glands, de-superheaters, de-aerators and so on. These can be found in detail in textbooks devoted to practical steam power plant.

# 5.4 Gas turbine engines

In this section we will examine how practical gas turbine engine sets vary from the basic Joule cycle.

The efficiency of gas turbine engines increases with pressure/compression ratio. In practice this is limited, as the type of compressor needed to produce very large flows of air cannot do so at high pressures (6 bar is a typical pressure for the combustion chamber). The efficiency of gas turbines may be improved by the use of intercooling and heat exchangers.

## 5.4.1 *Gas constants*

Although air is used in the compressor, the gas going through the turbine contains products of combustion so the adiabatic index and specific heat capacity are different in the turbine and compressor.

## 5.4.2 *Free turbines*

Most designs used for gas turbine sets use two turbines – one to drive the compressor and a free turbine. The free turbine drives the load and it is not connected directly to the compressor. It may also run at a different speed to the compressor. Figure 5.23 shows the layouts for parallel and series turbines.

**Fig. 5.23** *Layouts of a gas turbine with a free turbine*

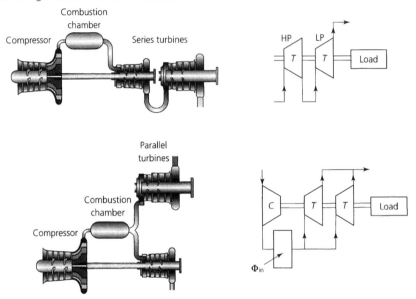

## 5.4.3 *Intercooling and reheating*

Basically, if the air is compressed in stages and cooled between each stage, then the work of compression is reduced and the efficiency is increased. The reverse theory also applies. If several stages of turbine expansions are used and the gas is reheated between stages, the power output and efficiency are increased (Fig. 5.24).

**Fig. 5.24** *Symbolic representation of a gas turbine with reheating and intercooling*

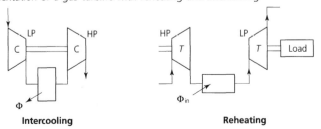

A gas turbine draws in air from atmosphere at 1 bar and 10 °C and compresses it to 5 bar. The air is heated to 1200 K at constant pressure and is then expanded through two stages in series back to 1 bar. The high-pressure turbine is connected to the compressor and produces just enough power to drive it. The low-pressure stage is connected to an external load and produces 80 kW of power.

1.  Draw the circuit.
2.  Calculate the mass flow of air, the interstage pressure of the turbines and the thermal efficiency of the cycle. Assume $\gamma = 1.4$ and $c_p = 1.005$ kJ/kg K for both the turbines and the compressor. Neglect the increase in mass due to the addition of fuel for burning.
3.  Compare the efficiency to the air standard efficiency.

*Solution*

**Fig. 5.25**  *Gas turbine with a free turbine*

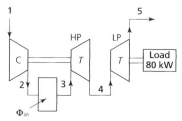

*Compressor*

$$T_2 = T_1 r_p^{1-1/\gamma} = 283 \times 5^{0.286} = 448.4 \text{ K}$$

Power input to compressor $= mc_p(T_2 - T_1)$
Power output of h.p. turbine $= mc_p(T_3 - T_4)$

Since these are equal we may equate them:

$$1.005(448.4 - 283) = 1.005(1200 - T_4) \qquad \text{hence:} \quad T_4 = 1034.6 \text{ K}$$

*High-pressure turbine*

$$\frac{T_4}{T_3} = \left(\frac{p_4}{p_5}\right)^{1-1/\gamma}$$

$$\frac{T_4}{T_5} = \frac{1034.6}{1200} = 0.595 = \left(\frac{p_4}{5}\right)^{0.286} \qquad p_4 = 5 \times 0.595^{1/0.286} = 2.977 \text{ bar}$$

*Low-pressure turbine*

$$\frac{T_5}{T_4} = \left(\frac{1}{2.977}\right)^{1-1/\gamma} = 0.336^{0.286} = 0.732 \qquad T_5 = 757.3 \text{ K}$$

### Net power

The net power is 80 kW.

$$80 = mc_p(T_4 - T_5) = m \times 1.005(1034.6 - 757.3)$$
$$m = \mathbf{0.288 \ kg/s}$$

### Heat input

$$\Phi_{in} = mc_p(T_3 - T_2) = 0.288 \times 1.005(1200 - 448.4) = 217.5 \ kW$$

### Thermal efficiency

$$\eta_{th} = P_{net}/\Phi_{in} = 80/219.9 = 0.367 \ or \ 36.7\%$$

The air standard efficiency is the Joule efficiency:

$$\eta = 1 - r_p^{-0.286} = 1 - 5^{-0.286} = 0.369 \ or \ 36.9\%$$

---

### SELF-ASSESSMENT EXERCISE 5.7

1.  A gas turbine draws in air from atmosphere at 1 bar and 15 °C and compresses it to 4.5 bar. The air is heated to 1100 K at constant pressure and then expanded through two stages in series back to 1 bar. The high-pressure turbine is connected to the compressor and produces just enough power to drive it. The low-pressure stage is connected to an external load and produces 100 kW of power.

    For the compressor $\gamma = 1.4$ and for the turbines $\gamma = 1.3$. The gas constant is 0.287 kJ/kg K for both.

    Neglect the increase in mass due to the addition of fuel for burning. Assume that the specific heat of the gas in the combustion chamber is the same as that for the turbines, and calculate:
    (a) The specific heat $c_p$ of the air and the burned mixture.
    (b) The mass flow of air.
    (c) The interstage pressure of the turbines.
    (d) The thermal efficiency of the cycle.

2.  A gas turbine draws in air from atmosphere at 1 bar and 300 K and compresses it to 6 bar. The air is heated to 1300 K at constant pressure and then expanded through two stages in series back to 1 bar. The high-pressure turbine is connected to the compressor and produces just enough power to drive it.

    $\gamma = 1.4$ and $R = 0.287$ kJ/kg K for both the turbine and compressor. Neglect the increase in mass due to the addition of fuel for burning and calculate the following for a mass flow of 1 kg/s:
    (a) The interstage pressure.
    (b) The net power output.
    (c) The thermal efficiency of the cycle.

---

### 5.4.4 *Exhaust gas heat exchanger*

The exhaust gas from a turbine is hotter than the air leaving the compressor. If heat is passed to the air from the exhaust gas, then less fuel is needed in the combustion chamber to raise the air to the operating temperature. This requires an exhaust heat exchanger. Figure 5.26 shows the layout required.

**Fig. 5.26**  *Symbolic representation of a gas turbine with an exhaust heat exchanger*

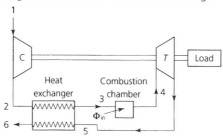

In order to solve problems associated with this cycle, it is necessary to determine the temperature prior to the combustion chamber ($T_3$).

A perfect heat exchanger would heat up the air to make $T_3$ the same as $T_5$. It would also cool down the exhaust gas and $T_6$ would equal $T_2$. In reality this is not possible so the concept of **thermal ratio** is used. This is defined as the ratio of the enthalpy given to the air to the maximum possible enthalpy lost by the exhaust gas. The enthalpy lost by the exhaust gas is

$$\Delta H = m_g c_{pg}(T_5 - T_6)$$

This would be a maximum if the gas is cooled down such that $T_6 = T_2$. Of course in reality this does not occur, the maximum is not achieved, and the gas turbine does not perform as well as predicted by this idealisation.

$$\Delta H(\text{maximum}) = m_g c_{pg}(T_5 - T_2)$$

The enthalpy gained by the air is

$$\Delta H(\text{air}) = m_a c_{pa}(T_3 - T_2)$$

Hence the thermal ratio is

$$\text{TR} = m_a c_{pa}(T_3 - T_2)/m_g c_{pg}(T_5 - T_2)$$

The suffix 'a' refers to the air and 'g' to the exhaust gas. Since the mass of fuel added in the combustion chamber is small compared to the air flow we often neglect the difference in mass and the equation becomes

$$\text{TR} = c_{pa}(T_3 - T_2)/c_{pg}(T_5 - T_2)$$

A gas turbine uses a pressure ratio of 7.5/1. The inlet temperature and pressure are respectively 10 °C and 105 kPa. The temperature after heating in the combustion chamber is 1300 °C. The specific heat capacity $c_p$ for air is 1.005 kJ/kg K and for the exhaust gas is 1.15 kJ/kg K. The adiabatic index is 1.4 for air and 1.33 for the gas. Assume isentropic compression and expansion. The mass flow rate is 1kg/s.

Calculate the air standard efficiency if no heat exchanger is used and compare it to the thermal efficiency when an exhaust heat exchanger with a thermal ratio of 0.8 is used.

### Solution
Referring to the numbers used on Fig. 5.26, the solution is as follows:

$$\text{Air standard efficiency} = 1 - r_p^{1-1/\gamma} = 1 - 7.5^{-0.286} = \textbf{0.438 or 43.8\%}$$

Solution with heat exchanger:

$$T_2 = T_1 r_p^{1-1/\gamma} = 283(7.5)^{0.286} = 503.6 \text{ K}$$
$$T_5 = T_4/r_p^{1-1/\gamma} = 1573/(7.5)^{0.248} = 954.1 \text{ K}$$

Use the thermal ratio to find $T_3$:

$$\begin{aligned} 0.8 &= 1.005(T_3 - T_2)/1.15(T_5 - T_2) \\ &= 1.005(T_3 - 503.6)/1.15(954.1 - 503.6) \\ \therefore \quad T_3 &= 916 \text{ K} \end{aligned}$$

In order find the thermal efficiency, it is best to solve the energy transfers:

$$\begin{aligned} P_{in} &= mc_{pa}(T_2 - T_1) = 1 \times 1.005(503.6 - 283) = 221.7 \text{ kW} \\ P_{out} &= mc_{pg}(T_4 - T_5) = 1 \times 1.15(1573 - 954.1) = 711.7 \text{ kW} \\ P_{net} &= P_{out} - P_{in} = 490 \text{ kW} \\ \Phi_{in} \text{ combustion chamber} &= mc_{pg}(T_4 - T_3) \\ &= 1.15(1573 - 916) = 755.5 \text{ kW} \end{aligned}$$

$$\eta_{th} = P_{net}/\Phi_{in} = 490/755.5 = \textbf{0.65 or 65\%}$$

1.  A gas turbine uses a pressure ratio of 7/1. The inlet temperature and pressure are respectively 10 °C and 100 kPa. The temperature after heating in the combustion chamber is 1000 °C. The specific heat capacity $c_p$ is 1.005 kJ/kg K and the adiabatic index is 1.4 for air and gas. Assume isentropic compression and expansion. The mass flow rate is 0.7 kg/s.

    Calculate the net power output and the thermal efficiency when an exhaust heat exchanger with a thermal ratio of 0.8 is used.

# 5.5 Isentropic efficiency

## 5.5.1 *The effect of friction*

When a fluid is expanded or compressed with fluid friction occurring, a degree of irreversibility is present. The result is the generation of internal heat equivalent to a heat transfer. **This always results in an increase in entropy.**

Figure 5.27 shows expansion and compression processes on a *T–s* diagram. In the case of vapour, the line crosses the saturation curve. In the case of gas, the process takes place well away from the saturation curve and indeed the saturation curve would not normally be shown for gas processes. Note that, in every case, the ideal process is from 1 to 2′ but the real process is from 1 to 2.

Friction does the following:

- Increases the entropy.
- Increases the enthalpy.
- The true process path on property diagrams is always to the right of the ideal process.
- When the final point, 2, is in the gas (superheat) region, the result is a hotter temperature.
- When the final point, 2, is in the wet region, the result is a dryer vapour.

Gas and vapour processes should be described by sketching them on an appropriate property diagram with these effects of friction clearly shown.

**Fig. 5.27** *T–s diagrams showing the effect of friction on isentropic processes*

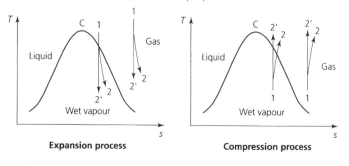

Expansion process     Compression process

The same points are also apparent on the $h$–$s$ diagram. Figure 5.28 shows a vapour expansion from 1 to 2 with the ideal being from 1 to 2′. Note how it ends up dryer at the same pressure with an increase in entropy. Vapour is not normally compressed, so this is not shown.

**Fig. 5.28** *h–s diagram showing the effect of friction on isentropic processes*

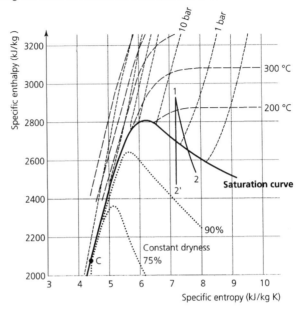

### 5.5.2 *Isentropic efficiency*

An ideal reversible adiabatic process would be constant entropy, as shown on the diagrams from 1 to 2′. When friction is present, the process is 1 to 2.

The ideal change in enthalpy is: $\quad \Delta h(\text{ideal}) = h_{2'} - h_1$
The actual change is: $\quad\quad\quad\quad \Delta h(\text{actual}) = h_2 - h_1$

The isentropic efficiency is defined as follows:

*Expansion* $\quad\quad \eta_{is} = \dfrac{\Delta h(\text{actual})}{\Delta h(\text{ideal})} = \dfrac{h_2 - h_1}{h_{2'} - h_1}$

*Compression* $\quad \eta_{is} = \dfrac{\Delta h(\text{ideal})}{\Delta h(\text{actual})} = \dfrac{h_{2'} - h_1}{h_2 - h_1}$

For gas only $h = c_p T$:

*Expansion* $\quad\quad \eta_{is} = \dfrac{T_2 - T_1}{T_{2'} - T_1}$

*Compression* $\quad \eta_{is} = \dfrac{T_{2'} - T_1}{T_2 - T_1}$

Note that, for an expansion, negative changes are obtained on the top and bottom lines that cancel.

If the work transfer rate is only due to the change in enthalpy we may also define isentropic efficiency as follows:

$$\eta_{is} = \frac{\text{actual power output}}{\text{ideal power output}} \quad \text{for a turbine}$$

$$\eta_{is} = \frac{\text{ideal power input}}{\text{actual power input}} \quad \text{for a compressor}$$

## WORKED EXAMPLE 5.11

A turbine expands steam adiabatically from 70 bar and 500 °C to 0.1 bar with an isentropic efficiency of 0.9. The power output is 35 MW. Determine the steam flow rate.

### Solution
The solution is easier with a $h$–$s$ chart, but we will do it with tables only.

$h_1 = 3410$ kJ/kg at 70 bar and 500 °C.
$s_1 = 6.796$ kJ/kg K at 70 bar and 500 °C.

For an ideal expansion from 1 to 2′ we calculate the dryness fraction as follows:

$s_1 = s_2 = s_f + x's_{fg}$ at 0.1 bar.
$6.796 = 0.649 + x'(7.5) \qquad x' = 0.8196$

Note that you can never be certain if the steam will go wet. It may still be super-heated after expansion. If $x'$ was found to be larger than unity, then because this is impossible, it must be superheated and you need to deduce its temperature by referring to the superheat tables.

Now we find the ideal enthalpy $h_{2'}$:

$h_{2'} = h_f + x'h_{fg}$ at 0.1 bar.
$\quad = 192 + 0.8196(2392) = 2152.2$ kJ/kg

Now we use the isentropic efficiency to find the actual enthalpy $h_2$:

$$\eta_{is} = \frac{\Delta h(\text{ideal})}{\Delta h(\text{actual})}$$
$$0.9 = \frac{2152.2 - 3410}{h_2 - 3410}$$
$$\therefore \quad h_2 = 2278.3 \text{ kJ/kg}$$

Now we may use the SFEE to find the mass flow rate:

$\Phi + P = m(h_2 - h_1)$
$\Phi = 0$ since it is an adiabatic process.
$P = -35\,000$ kW (out of system) $= m(2278.3 - 3410)$
$m = \mathbf{30.926 \ kg/s}$

A turbine expands gas adiabatically from 1 MPa and 600 °C to 100 kPa. The isentropic efficiency is 0.92. The mass flow rate is 12 kg/s. Calculate the power output.

$$c_p = 1.005 \text{ kJ/kg K} \qquad c_v = 0.718 \text{ kJ/kg K}$$

*Solution*

The process is adiabatic so the ideal temperature $T_{2'}$ is given by:

$$T_{2'} = T_1(r_p)^{1-1/\gamma}$$

$r_p$ is the pressure ratio $= p_2/p_1 = 0.1$

$$\gamma = c_p/c_v = 1.005/0.718 = 1.4$$
$$T_{2'} = 873(0.1)^{1-1/1.4} = 451.9 \text{ K}$$

Now we use the isentropic efficiency to find the actual final temperature:

$$\eta_{is} = (T_2 - T_1)/(T_{2'} - T_1)$$
$$0.92 = (T_2 - 873)/(451.9 - 873)$$
$$\therefore T_2 = 485.6 \text{ K}$$

Now we use the SFEE to find the power output:

$$\Phi + P = mc_p(T_2 - T_1)$$

The process is adiabatic, so $\Phi = 0$.

$$P = 12(1.005)(485.6 - 873) = \mathbf{-4672 \text{ kW}} \text{ (out of system)}$$

A simple steam power plant uses the Rankine cycle. The boiler supplies super-heated steam to the turbine at 40 bar and 400 °C. The condenser operates at 0.2 bar and produces saturated water. The power input to the pump is negligible.

1. Calculate the thermal efficiency of the ideal cycle.
2. Calculate the thermal efficiency when the turbine has an isentropic efficiency of 89%.

*Solution*

The solution is easier with a *h–s* chart.

*Ideal conditions*

From the chart: $h_1 = 3210 \text{ kJ/kg}$ and $h_2 = 2230 \text{ kJ/kg/k}$
The ideal work output $= 3210 - 2230 = 980 \text{ kJ/kg}$

**Fig. 5.29** *Isentropic expansion on the h–s diagram*

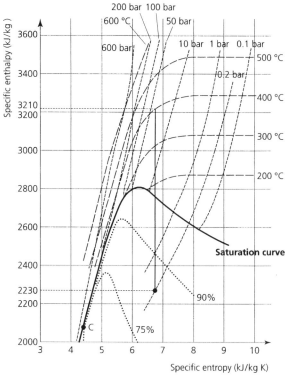

When the power input to the pump is ignored, the power out is the net power and the enthalpy at inlet to the boiler is $h_f$ at 0.2 bar.

The heat input to the boiler = 3210 − 251 = 2959 kJ/kg

$$\eta_{th} = 980/2959 = \textbf{0.331 or 33.1\%}$$

*Taking account of isentropic efficiency*

$$\eta_{is} = \frac{\text{actual work output}}{\text{ideal work output}} = \frac{\text{actual work output}}{980}$$

$$0.89 = \frac{\text{actual work output}}{980}$$

Actual work output = 980 × 0.89 = 872.2 kJ/kg

$$\eta_{th} = 872.2/2959 = \textbf{0.295 or 29.5\%}$$

A simple gas turbine uses the Joule cycle. The pressure ratio is 6.5. The air temperature is 300 K at inlet to the compressor and 1373 K at inlet to the turbine. The adiabatic index is 1.4 throughout and the specific heat capacities may be considered constant.

1. Calculate the thermal efficiency of the ideal cycle.
2. Calculate the thermal efficiency when the turbine and compressor has an isentropic efficiency of 90%.
3. Sketch the cycle on a $T$–$s$ diagram showing the effect of friction.

### Solution

#### Ideal cycle
Compressor:  $T_2 = 300(6.5)^{0.286} = 512.4$ K
Turbine:  $T_4 = 1373(6.5)^{-0.286} = 803.8$ K

$$\eta_{th} = 1 - \frac{T_4 - T_1}{T_3 - T_2} = 1 - \frac{803.8 - 300}{1373 - 512.4} = \textbf{0.415 or 41.5\%}$$

#### Including isentropic efficiency
Compressor:  $\eta_{is} = 0.9 = \dfrac{512.4 - 300}{T_2 - 300}$   $T_2 = 536$ K

Turbine:  $\eta_{is} = 0.9 = \dfrac{1373 - T_4}{1373 - 803.8}$   $T_4 = 860.7$ K

$$\eta_{th} = 1 - \frac{T_4 - T_1}{T_3 - T_2} = 1 - \frac{860.7 - 300}{1373 - 536} = \textbf{0.33 or 33\%}$$

**Fig. 5.30**  *The affect of friction on the Joule cycle*

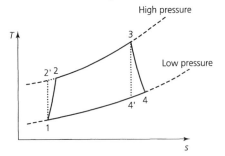

1. Steam is expanded adiabatically in a turbine from 100 bar and 600 °C to 0.09 bar with an isentropic efficiency of 0.88. The mass flow rate is 40 kg/s. Calculate the power output.

2. A compressor takes in gas at 1 bar and 15 °C and compresses it adiabatically to 10 bar with an isentropic efficiency of 0.89. The mass flow rate is 5 kg/s. Calculate the final temperature and the power input. ($c_p = 1.005$ kJ/kg K and $\gamma = 1.4$)

3. A turbine is supplied with 3 kg/s of hot gas at 10 bar and 920 °C. It expands adiabatically to 1 bar with an isentropic efficiency of 0.92. Calculate the final temperature and the power output. ($c_p = 1.005$ kJ/kg K and $\gamma = -1.4$)

4. A turbine is supplied with 7 kg/s of hot gas at 9 bar and 850 °C that it expands adiabatically to 1 bar with an isentropic efficiency of 0.87. Calculate the final temperature and the power output. ($c_p = 1.005$ kJ/kg K and $\gamma = 1.4$)

5. A simple steam power plant uses the Rankine cycle. The boiler supplies superheated steam to the turbine at 100 bar and 550 °C. The condenser operates at 0.05 bar and produces saturated water. The power input to the pump is negligible.
   (a) Calculate the thermal efficiency of the ideal cycle.
   (b) Calculate the thermal efficiency when the turbine has an isentropic efficiency of 85%.

6. A simple gas turbine uses the Joule cycle. The pressure ratio is 7.5. The air temperature is 288 K at inlet to the compressor and 1400 K at inlet to the turbine. The adiabatic index is 1.4 throughout and the specific heat capacities may be considered constant.
   (a) Calculate the thermal efficiency of the ideal cycle.
   (b) Calculate the thermal efficiency when the turbine and compressor have an isentropic efficiency of 92%.

# Appendix A: Entropy changes for perfect gas processes in closed systems

Consider a closed system expansion of a fluid against a piston with heat and work transfer taking place (Fig. A.1).

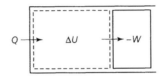

Applying the non-flow energy equation we have

$$Q + W = \Delta U$$

Differentiating we have

$$dQ + dW = dU$$

Since $dQ = T\,dS$ and $dW = -p\,dV$, then

$$T\,dS - p\,dV = dU \quad \text{and} \quad T\,dS = dU + p\,dV$$

This expression is the starting point for all derivations of entropy changes for any fluid (gas or vapour) in closed systems. It is normal to use specific properties so the equation becomes

$$T\,ds = du + p\,dv$$

but from the gas law $pv = RT$ we may substitute for $p$ and the equation becomes

$$T\,ds = du + RT\frac{dv}{v}$$

Rearranging and substituting $du = c_v\,dT$ we have

$$ds = c_v\frac{dT}{T} + R\frac{dv}{v} \tag{A.1}$$

where $s$ is the specific entropy, $v$ is the specific volume, and $u$ is the specific internal energy.

# A.1 Isothermal process

**Fig. A.2** *Constant temperature process*

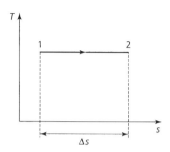

In the isothermal process (Fig. A.2) the temperature is constant. Starting with equation (A.1)

$$ds = c_v \frac{dT}{T} + R \frac{dv}{v}$$

since $dT = 0$ then

$$ds = R \frac{dv}{v}$$

and integrating between limits 1 and 2 we have

$$s_2 - s_1 = \Delta s = R \ln\left(\frac{v_2}{v_1}\right)$$

A quicker alternative derivation is as follows:

$$Q + W = \Delta U$$

Since $\Delta U = 0$, then $Q = -W$.

It was shown in the text on work laws that $W = -mRT \ln(V_2/V_1)$

$$Q = \int T \, dS = T \, \Delta S$$

but $T$ is constant, therefore:

$$\Delta S = \frac{Q}{T} = -\frac{W}{T} = \frac{mRT}{T} \ln\left(\frac{V_2}{V_1}\right)$$
$$= mRT \ln\left(\frac{V_2}{V_1}\right)$$

Also

$$\frac{V_2}{V_1} = \frac{p_1}{p_2}$$

Hence:

$$\Delta S = mRT \ln\left(\frac{p_1}{p_2}\right)$$

---

The change in specific entropy is obtained by dividing by mass:

$$\Delta s = R \ln\left(\frac{V_2}{V_1}\right) \quad \text{or} \quad \Delta S = R \ln\left(\frac{p_1}{p_2}\right)$$

## A.2 Constant volume process

**Fig. A.3** *Constant volume process*

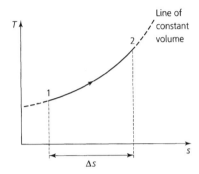

Referring to Fig. A.3, and starting again with equation (A.1) we have

$$ds = c_v\left(\frac{dT}{T}\right) + R\left(\frac{dv}{v}\right)$$

In this case, $dv = 0$ so

$$ds = c_v\left(\frac{dT}{T}\right)$$

Integrating between limits 1 and 2:

$$\Delta s = c_v \ln\left(\frac{T_2}{T_1}\right)$$

## A.3 Constant pressure process

**Fig. A.4** *Constant pressure process*

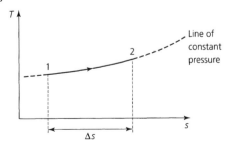

Referring to Fig. A.4, and starting again with equation (A.1) we have

$$ds = c_v \left( \frac{dT}{T} \right) + R \left( \frac{dv}{v} \right)$$

In this case we integrate and obtain

$$\Delta s = c_v \ln \left( \frac{T_2}{T_1} \right) + R \ln \left( \frac{v_2}{v_1} \right)$$

For a constant pressure process the gas law tells us that $v/T$ = constant, hence

$$\frac{T_2}{T_1} = \frac{v_2}{v_1}$$

so the expression becomes

$$\Delta s = c_v \ln \left( \frac{T_2}{T_1} \right) + R \ln \left( \frac{T_2}{T_1} \right)$$

$$= (c_v + R) \ln \left( \frac{T_2}{T_1} \right)$$

It was shown in an earlier tutorial that $R = c_p - c_v$, hence

$$\Delta s = c_p \ln \left( \frac{T_2}{T_1} \right)$$

## A.4 Polytropic process

This is the most difficult of all the derivations here. Since all the foregoing are particular examples of the polytropic process, the resulting formula should apply to them also (Fig. A.5).

**Fig. A.5** *Entropy change by two routes*

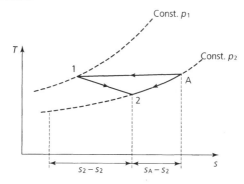

The polytropic expansion is from 1 to 2 on the $T$–$s$ diagram with different pressures, volumes and temperatures at the two points. The derivation is done in two stages by supposing that the change takes place first at constant temperature from 1 to A and then at constant pressure from A to 2. You could use a constant volume process instead of constant pressure if you wish.

$$s_2 - s_1 = (s_A - s_1) - (s_A - s_2)$$
$$= (s_A - s_1) + (s_2 - s_A)$$

For the constant temperature process

$$(s_A - s_1) = R \ln\left(\frac{p_1}{p_A}\right)$$

For the constant pressure process

$$s_2 - s_A = c_p \ln\left(\frac{T_2}{T_A}\right)$$

$$s_2 - s_1 = R \ln\left(\frac{p_1}{p_A}\right) + c_p \ln\left(\frac{T_2}{T_A}\right)$$

$$p_A = p_2 \quad \text{and} \quad T_A = T_1$$

$$\Delta s = s_2 - s_1 = R \ln\left(\frac{p_1}{p_2}\right) + c_p \ln\left(\frac{T_2}{T_1}\right)$$

Divide through by $R$:

$$\frac{\Delta s}{R} = \ln\left(\frac{p_1}{p_2}\right) + \frac{c_p}{R} \ln\left(\frac{T_2}{T_1}\right)$$

From the relationship between $c_p$, $R$ and $\gamma$ we have $c_p/R = \gamma/(\gamma - 1)$:

$$\frac{\Delta s}{R} = \ln\left(\frac{p_1}{p_2}\right) + \frac{\gamma}{\gamma - 1} \ln\left(\frac{T_2}{T_1}\right)$$

$$= \ln\left(\frac{p_1}{p_2}\right)\left(\frac{T_2}{T_1}\right)^{\gamma/(\gamma-1)}$$

This formula is for a polytropic process and should also work for isothermal, constant pressure, constant volume and adiabatic processes. In other words, it must be the derivation for the entropy change of a perfect gas for any closed system process.

## WORKED EXAMPLE A.1

A perfect gas is expanded from 5 bar to 1 bar by the law $pV^{1.2} = C$. The initial temperature is 200 °C. Calculate the change in specific entropy. ($R$ = 287 J/kg K; $\gamma = 1.4$)

## Solution

$$T_2 = 473\left(\frac{1}{5}\right)^{1-1/1.2} = 361.7 \text{ K}$$

$$\frac{\Delta s}{R} = \ln\left(\frac{p_1}{p_2}\right)\left(\frac{T_2}{T_1}\right)^{\gamma/\gamma-1} = \ln\left(\frac{5}{1}\right)\left(\frac{361.7}{473}\right)^{3.5} = 0.671$$

$$\Delta s = 0.671 \times 287 = \textbf{192.5 J/kg K}$$

## SELF-ASSESSMENT EXERCISE A.1

1. Calculate the specific entropy change when a perfect gas undergoes a reversible isothermal expansion from 500 kPa to 100 kPa. ($R = 287$ J/kg K)

2. Calculate the total entropy change when 2 kg of perfect gas is compressed reversibly and isothermally from 9 dm³ to 1 dm³. ($R = 300$ J/kg K)

3. Calculate the change in entropy when 2.5 kg of perfect gas is heated from 20 °C to 100 °C at constant volume. (Take $c_v = 780$ J/kg K)

4. Calculate the total entropy change when 5 kg of gas is expanded at constant pressure from 30 °C to 200 °C. ($R = 300$ J/kg K; $c_v = 800$ J/kg K)

5. A perfect gas is expanded from 5 bar to 1 bar by the law $pV^{1.6} = C$. The initial temperature is 200 °C. Calculate the change in specific entropy. ($R = 287$ J/kg K; $\gamma = 1.4$)

6. A perfect gas is expanded reversibly and adiabatically from 5 bar to 1 bar by the law $pV^{\gamma} = C$. The initial temperature is 200 °C. Calculate the change in specific entropy using the formula for a polytropic process. ($R = 287$ J/kg K; $\gamma = 1.4$)

# Appendix B: Closed system vapour processes

## B.1 Isentropic process

When a vapour undergoes a reversible adiabatic process, the entropy is constant. An expansion or compression will be a vertical line on the $T$–$s$ diagram, as shown (line A on Fig. B.1).

**Fig. B.1** *Constant entropy, temperature and pressure process on a T–s diagram*

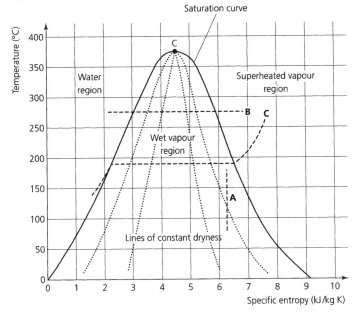

---

**WORKED EXAMPLE B.1**

Steam at 40 bar and 300 °C is expanded reversibly and adiabatically (isentropically) to 4 bar. Calculate the dryness fraction after the expansion.

### Solution

The key to this is that the specific entropy is the same before and after the expansion.

$s_1$ at 40 bar and 300 °C is 6.364 kJ/kg K.
$s_2$ at 4 bar and assumed wet is $s_f + x s_{fg} = s_1$

$$6.364 = 1.776 + x(5.121)$$
$$x = 0.896$$

### SELF-ASSESSMENT EXERCISE B.1

1. Steam at 100 bar and 400 °C is expanded reversibly and adiabatically (isentropically) to 1 bar. Calculate the dryness fraction after the expansion.

2. Steam at 70 bar and 500 °C is expanded reversibly and adiabatically (isentropically) to 0.05 bar. Calculate the dryness fraction after the expansion.

## B.2 Isothermal process

This will be a horizontal line on the $T$–$s$ graph (line B on Fig. B.1). Since the temperature is constant the entropy change is simply $\Delta S = Q/T$.

### WORKED EXAMPLE B.2

Steam at 15 bar and 400 °C is heated isothermally and the pressure is raised to 30 bar in a closed system. Calculate the specific entropy change, the heat transfer and the work done.

### Solution
$s_1 = 7.268$ at 15 bar and 400 °C
$s_2 = 6.921$ at 30 bar and 400 °C

$$\Delta s = 6.921 - 7.268 = -0.347 \text{ kJ/kg K}$$
$$T = 400 + 273 = 673 \text{ K}$$
$$Q = T \Delta s = 673(-0.347) = -206.6 \text{ kJ/kg}$$

From the non-flow energy equation we have $Q + W = \Delta U$. We must look up the internal energy values from the tables.

$u_1 = 2952$ kJ/kg K at 15 bar and 400 °C
$u_2 = 3231$ kJ/kg K at 30 bar and 400 °C
$\therefore \quad \Delta u = 3231 - 2952 = 279 \text{ kJ/kg}$
$W = \Delta u - Q = 279 - (206.6) = 485.6 \text{ kJ/kg}$
$\quad = 485.6$ kJ/kg into the system (since it is positive)

# B.3 Constant pressure process

A constant pressure line is shown on the $T$–$s$ graph (line C on Fig. B.1). The entropy change can only be found by looking up the values.

---

**WORKED EXAMPLE B.3**

3 kg of wet steam is heated from 9 bar and 0.96 dry until it is superheated at 9 bar and 300 °C. Calculate the work done, the heat transfer and the change in entropy.

*Solution*

$V_1 = mxv_g$ at 9 bar $= 3(0.96)(0.2148) = 0.619$ m$^3$
$V_2 = mv$ at 9 bar and 300 °C $= 3(0.2874) = 0.862$ m$^3$
$W = -9 \times 10^5 (0.862 - 0.619) = -218.88 \times 10^3$ J or **−218.88 kJ**

$U_1 = m(u_f + xu_{fg})$ at 9 bar $= 3[742 + 0.96(1839)] = 7522$ kJ
$U_2 = mu$ at 9 bar and 300 °C $= 3(2796) = 8388$ kJ
$\Delta U = 8388 - 7522 = 866$ kJ
$Q = \Delta U - W = 866 - (-218.88) =$ **1085 kJ** (into system)

$S_1 = m(s_f + xs_{fg})$ at 9 bar $= 3[2.094 + 0.96(4.529)] = 19.325$ kJ/K
$S_2 = ms$ at 9 bar and 300 °C $= 3(7.176) = 21.528$ kJ/K
$\Delta S = 21.528 - 19.325 =$ **2.2 kJ/K**

---

# B.4 Constant volume process

In this case since there is no change of volume there is no work done (in a closed system). It follows that $Q = \Delta U$.

The only way to find the change in entropy is to look up the values.

---

**WORKED EXAMPLE B.4**

Steam at 10 bar and dry saturated is cooled down at constant volume to 5 bar. The mass of steam is 1 kg. Calculate the heat transfer and the change in entropy.

*Solution*

$v_1 = 0.1944$ m$^3$/kg ($v_g$ at 10 bar).
$v_2 = v_1 = 0.1944$ m$^3$/kg

We make an assumption about the final condition and it is likely that the steam will partially condense on cooling and end up as wet steam.

$v_2 = xv_g$ at 5 bar $= x(0.3748) = 0.1944$ m$^3$/kg
$\therefore \quad x = 0.1944/0.3748 = 0.5187$

---

$u_1 = 2584$ kJ/kg ($u_g$ at 10 bar)

$u_2 = u_f + xu_{fg}$ at 5 bar $= 639 + (0.5187)(2562 - 639) = 1636.5$ kJ/kg

$Q = \Delta U = 1$ kg$(1636.5 - 2584) = $ **−895.5 kJ** (out of system)

$s_1 = 6.585$ kJ/kg K ($s_g$ at 10 bar)

$s_2 = s_f + xs_{fg}$ at 5 bar $= 1.860 + (0.5187)(4.962) = 4.433$ kJ/kg K

$\Delta S = 1$ kg $\times (4.433 - 6.585) = $ **−2.151 kJ/K**

*Note*: This should be negative if $Q$ is negative.

# B.5 Polytropic process

Again, we can only find entropy changes by looking up the values. There is no formula for vapour.

## WORKED EXAMPLE B.5

2 kg of steam at 40 bar and 300 °C is expanded reversibly to 5 bar by the law $pV^{1.2} = $ constant. Calculate the heat transfer, the work transfer and the change in entropy.

### Solution

$V_1 = mv$ at 40 bar and 300 °C $= 2(0.0588) = 0.1176$ m³

$40 \times 0.1176^{1.2} = 5V_2^{1.2}$

$$\frac{40}{5} = \left(\frac{V_2}{0.1176}\right)^{1.2}$$

$$8^{1/1.2} = \frac{V_2}{0.1176}$$

$$5.656 = \frac{V_2}{0.1176}$$

$V_2 = 0.665$ m³:       $V_2 = 0.665 = xmv_g$ at 5 bar $= x(2)(0.3748)$

$\therefore$   $x = $ **0.887** after the expansion (steam has gone wet)

$W = [(5 \times 10^5)(0.665) - (40 \times 10^5)(0.1176)]/(1.2 - 1)$
     $= $ **−689.5 kJ** (out of system)

$U_1 = mu$ at 40 bar and 300 °C $= 2(2728) = 5456$ kJ

$U_2 = m(u_f + xu_{fg})$ at 5 bar $= 2[639 + 0.887(1923)] = 4689$ kJ

$\therefore$   $\Delta U = 4689 - 5456 = -767$ kJ

$Q = \Delta U - W = -767 - (-689.5) = $ **−77.5** (out of system)

$S_2 = m(s_f + xs_{fg})$ at 5 bar $= 2[1.860 + 0.887(4.962)] = 12.523$ kJ/K

$S_1 = ms$ at 40 bar and 300 °C $= 2(6.364) = 12.72$ kJ/K

$\therefore$   $\Delta S = 12.523 - 12.72 = $ **−0.1974 kJ/K**

1.  5 kg of steam is expanded in a closed system at constant temperature from 5 bar and 400 °C to 2 bar and 400 °C. Calculate the change in entropy and the heat transfer.

2.  8 kg of steam is heated in a closed system at constant volume from 1 bar and 0.96 dry to 4 bar and 200 °C. Calculate the heat transfer and entropy change.

3.  6 kg of steam is cooled in a closed system at a constant pressure of 8 bar from 450 °C to 200 °C. Calculate the heat transfer and change in entropy.

4.  3 kg of steam is expanded by the law $pV^{1.25}$ = constant from 20 bar and 250 °C to 10 bar. Calculate the heat transfer, work transfer and entropy change.

# Answers to self-assessment exercises

## 1.1

1. 37.5 Watts

2. 8 MW

3. 1.57 MJ

4. (a) 216 W  (b) 256 kW

5. 24 m/s

6. (a) 6.76 m/s  (b) 38.9 W  (c) 1062.5 W

## 1.2

1. 1.226 kg/m$^3$

2. (a) 10 bar  (b) 11.892 kg/m$^3$

3. (a) 586 K  (b) 3.56 g

4. (a) 659 K  (b) 4.757 kg

5. (a) 212 cm$^3$  (b) 1.427 g

6. 0.595 kg/min

7. 6.148 kg

## 1.3

1. 11.49 kJ for both

2. −43 kJ, −60.3 kJ, −17.3 kJ

3. 8.7 MW

4. 30.15 kJ

5. (a) 11.9 g  (b) 1.537 kJ  (c) 2.151 kJ
   (d) 500 kPa  (e) 1.23 dm$^3$

## 1.4

1. 237.4 °C

2. 859 and 857 kJ/kg

3. 2794 and 2596 kJ/kg

4. 1935 kJ/kg

5. 3264 and 2957 kJ/kg

6. 0.09957 $m^3$/kg

7. 0.0697 $m^3$/kg

8. 2232 and 2092.1 kJ/kg

9. 0.2351 $m^3$

10. 1.012 $m^3$, 7.61 MJ

11. 4.74 MJ

12. 5.69 MJ

13. 0.101 $m^3$

## 1.5

1. 7.761 kJ/kg K

2. 6.116 kJ/kg K

3. 6.092 kJ/kg K

4. 4.882 kJ/kg K

5. −1.21 kJ/kg K

## 2.1

1. (a)  7.91 m/s     (b)  31.3 Watts     (c)  2819 W

## 2.2

1. 188.5 kW

2. 95.5 Nm

---

## 2.3

1. +60 kJ
2. 140 kJ
3. 300 kW
4. −6 kW
5. (a)  −10.5 kW      (b)  −13.734 kW      (c)  1.234 kW

## 2.4

1. (a)  4J      (b)  −1 J      (c)  19.93 °C
2. (a)  70.35 kW      (b)  65.35 kW
3. (a)  856 kJ/kg      (b)  3373 kJ/kg      (c)  37.75 kW
4. 2.417 kW
5. 0.86 kW
6. (a)  2331 kJ/kg and 163 kJ/kg      (b)  4336 kW
7. 37.4 kW
8. −16.8 kJ

## 2.5

1. 0.63
2. (a)  111.4 cm$^3$      (b)  207 °C
3. (a)  0.506 MPa      (b)  314 °C

## 2.6

1. (a)  1000 °C      (b)  594 °C      (c)  386.3 °C      (d)  263.8 °C
2. (a)  15 °C      (b)  173 °C      (c)  222 °C      (d)  269 °C
3. (a)  434.2 K      (b)  2.027 kJ      (c)  2.838 kJ
4. (a)  828.3 K      (b)  −7.25 kJ      (c)  −10.72 kJ

## 2.7

1. (a) 0.6183 m$^3$ and 3 m$^3$      (b) 0.863
   (c) 2829 kJ/kg and 2388 kJ/kg      (d) −1324 kW

2. (a) 0.066 m$^3$/kg and 17.4 m$^3$/kg      (b) 0.411
   (c) 3287 kJ/kg and 1134.9 kJ/kg      (d) −3228.2 kW

3. (a) 1.39 m$^3$    (b) 1.97 kg    (c) 2053 kJ
   (d) 0.798    (e) 4172 kJ    (f) 2119 kJ

## 2.8

1. (a) 0.00282 m$^3$    (b) 0.00974 m$^3$    (c) −2.921 kJ

2. 3.67 kJ

3. −31.8 J

4. 2.9 kJ

5. −184.2 J

6. 1.463 and −3.24 kJ

7. 1.124 and 1944 J

## 2.9

1. (a) 0.126 dm$^3$    (b) 257 J    (c) 170 °C
   (d) 1.189 g    (e) 128 J    (f) −128 J

2. (a) 0.00985 m$^3$    (b) 0.058 m$^3$    (c) −27 kJ
   (d) −20.3 kJ    (e) 6.7 kJ

3. (a) 615.4 K    (b) 26.27 kJ    (c) −26.3 kJ

4. (a) $\Delta F = A \, \Delta p \quad \Delta x = \Delta V/A$
   $k = \Delta F/\Delta x = A^2 \, \Delta p/\Delta V$
   $\Delta p/\Delta V = k/A^2$
   (b) $\Delta p/\Delta V = 28\,800/0.012^2 = 200 \times 10^6$
   If $\Delta p = 0$ to 100 kPa then
   $\Delta V = 100 \times 10^3/200 \times 10^6$
   $\Delta V = 0.5 \times 10^{-3}$ m$^3$
   (c) (i) 0.00058 kg
   (ii) 300 kPa
   (iii) 2700 K
   (iv) −200 J
   (v) 917.3 J
   (vi) 1117.3 J

## 2.10

1. (a) 0.03888 m$^3$    (b) 0.264 m$^3$    (c) −62 kJ
   (d) 0.779    (e) −107.9 kJ    (f) −46 kJ

2. (a) 0.3748 m$^3$    (b) −165 kJ    (c) −187.1 kJ    (d) 22.1 kJ

3. (a) 0.3748 m$^3$    (b) −84 kJ    (c) 143.9 kJ    (d) −227.9 kJ

## 3.1

1. 33.3% and 40 MW

2. 10 kJ and 30 kJ

## 3.2

1. 25.2 MW

2. 3.8 MW

3. 11.2 MW

4. 218.5 kW

## 3.3

1. No, the maximum it can be is 71%

2. 67.9%

## 3.4

1. (a) 58.5%    (b) 1450 K    (c) 4.17 MPa    (d) 293 kJ/kg

2. (a) 9.88/1
   (b) (i) 833 kJ/kg
        (ii) 1906 K
        (iii) 6.64 MPa

3. (a) 59.4%    (b) 4.1 kJ/cycle    (c) 205 kW

4. 1.235 kg

5. 871 kJ/kg and 1129 kJ/kg

## 3.5

1. (a) 1.374    (b) 66%

2. (a) 57.6%    (b) 680 kJ/kg

3. (a) 2424 K    (b) 67.5%    (c) 864 kJ/kg

## 3.6

1. (a) 42.7%   (b) 206.7 kW   (c) 88.26 kW

2. (a) 48.2%   (b) 617.5 K   (c) 911 kW

3. (a) 46.7%   (b) 599 K   (c) 1.9157 MW

## 3.7

1. 149 kW

2. 45.4 g/s

## 3.8

1. (a) 47.12 kW   (b) 480 kPa   (c) 61 kW
   (d) 77.2%   (e) 28.6%

2. (a) 25.9%   (b) 88%   (c) 22.8%

3. (a) 30.5%   (b) 81.7%   (c) 25%

4. (a) 66.1%   (b) 23.8%   (c) 36%

## 3.9

1. 2.686 MW

2. 0.0752 kg/s

3. 3.233 kg/s

4. 3.12 kg/s

5. 0.1126 kg/s

6. 672 kW

7. 2.281 MW

8. 1.6 MW
   Cost for Option 1: £84.38 per hour
   Cost for Option 2: £51.48 per hour
   When deciding costs, the capital cost and running costs of the equipment should also be considered.

## 4.1

1. (a) 92.4%   (b) 208.2 W   (c) 172.9 W   (d) 83%

2. (a) 82.7%   (b) 14.74 kW   (c) 79.2%

3. (a) 45.6%   (b) 547.6 dm$^3$/min   (c) 2.83 kW   (d) 80%

## 4.2

1.  21.8 kW

2.  (a)  6.366 bar      (b)  32.84 kW           (c)  6.3 kW for both cylinders
    (d)  26.53 kW       (e)  31.1 and 5.24 dm$^3$

3.  (a)  10.06 m$^3$      (b)  12.17 kg      (c)  2.115

4.  (a)  3 bar          (b)  98.9%         (c)  7.77 m$^3$/min
    (d)  4.545 dm$^3$      (e)  191.2 mm      (f)  16 and 16.93 kW

## 5.1

1.  (a)  6.12 kW      (b)  20 N

2.  22.7 m/s

3.  173.6 kg/s

## 5.2

1.  (a)  43.6%      (b)  10.91 kW      (c)  14.09 kW

2.  (a)  34.3%      (b)  792 kW      (c)  1890 kW

## 5.3

1.  (a)  44.9 MW      (b)  225 kW      (c)  124 MW
    (d)  79 MW        (e)  36%

2.  (a)  4.6 MW       (b)  30 kW       (c)  10.5 MW
    (d)  5.9 MW       (e)  44%

3.  (a)  Practical steam power plants are based on the Rankine cycle rather than the
    Carnot cycle because it is impractical to compress wet steam and control the
    dryness fractions. The Rankine cycle produces greater quantities of power for
    the same plant size by using superheated steam and condensing the exhaust
    steam into water.
    (b)  (i)  29.7%
         (ii)  1.3 kg/s

## 5.4

1.  (a)  2.2 MW      (b)  8.26 MW      (c)  17.7 kW      (d)  26.3%

2.  (a)  6.0 MW      (b)  26.5 MW      (c)  22.5%

## 5.5

1.  (a)  25.6 kg/s      (b)  83.2 MW

2.  (a)  27.7 kg/s      (b)  30.5 kg/s

## 5.6

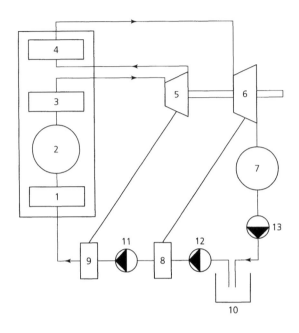

## 5.7

1. (a)  1.005 and 1.243 kJ/kg K  (b)  0.407 kg/s
   (c)  2.667 bar  (d)  30%

2. (a)  3.33 bar  (b)  322 kW  (c)  40%

## 5.8

1. 234 kW and 57%

2. (a)  40.8%  (b)  70.7%

## 5.9

1. 51 MW

2. 589.6 K and 1.513 MW

3. 663.5 K and 1.6 MW

4. 667 K and 3.2 MW

5. (a)  42.5%  (b)  36.1%

6. (a)  43.8%  (b)  36.9%

## A.1

1. +461.9 J/kg K

2. −1.32 kJ/k

3. 470 J/K

4. 2.45 kJ/K

5. −144 J/kg K

6. The answer should be zero since the process is constant entropy.

## B.1

1. 0.8107

2. 0.798

## B.2

1. 2.14 kJ/K and 1440 kJ

2. 180.5 kJ and 0.44 kJ/K

3. −3199 kJ and −5.436 kJ/K

4. 637.4 kJ, −55.4 kJ and 0.117 kJ/K

# Index